# Air Force

# Air Force
## The RAF in the 1990s

Robert Jackson

**Airlife**
England

Copyright © Robert Jackson, 1990

First published in the UK in 1990 by
Airlife Publishing Ltd.

British Library Cataloguing in Publication Data
Jackson, Robert
    Air force :the RAF in the 1990's.
    1.   Great Britain. Royal Air Force
    I.   Title
    358.400941

ISBN 1 85310 101 X

Printed in Singapore by Kyodo Printing Co. (Singapore) Pte. Ltd.

# Airlife Publishing Ltd.

101 Longden Road, Shrewsbury, SY3 9EB, England

# CONTENTS

# AUTHOR'S NOTE

Since this book was written, momentous political events in Eastern Europe appear, at least on the surface, to have forced a complete reappraisal of the established threat confronting NATO in general and the United Kingdom in particular. These changes should be borne in mind when reading this work.

What should also be borne firmly in mind is that while Europe passes through a period of great uncertainty, the continuing need for strong defence, and the constant vigilance that accompanies it, remains undiminished.

# INTRODUCTION

Although it has been argued that the state of today's Royal Air Force — in terms of organisation, role and equipment — is the result of policies laid down during the turbulent years of the mid-1960s, with the cancellation of major projects that were the core of the Service's future requirements at that time, and the rapid shift from global to European responsibilities, the basis for what is happening today, and for what is likely to happen tomorrow, was actually laid some years earlier.

The Defence White Paper of 1956 summed up the roles of the British Services as follows, in order of priority:

> They must make a contribution to the Allied deterrent commensurate with Britain's standing as a world power. This means not only building up and maintaining a nuclear stock-pile and the means of delivery, but also contributing to NATO's defensive effort by land, sea and air. Secondly, they must play their part in the cold war. By their mere presence they can contribute to the stability of the free world and the security of overseas territories whose peaceful development may be threatened by subversion, whether overtly Communist or masquerading as nationalism. Thirdly, they must be capable of dealing with outbreaks of limited war should these occur; and fourthly, they must also be capable of playing their part effectively in global war should it break out.

The text of the White Paper seemed logical enough, in view of the prevailing world political climate at that time. The advent of the hydrogen bomb had completely transformed the military situation; the policy of deterrence seemed to make the prospect of all-out war between East and West increasingly remote, and in turn rendered conventional forces, though still of great importance in some situations, a relatively less important factor in world affairs.

It was clear, however, that Britain could no longer, for economic reasons, continue to do as much as she had done in the past on the world military scene. This fact was underlined by the Suez Crisis of October–November 1956, which seriously overstretched the whole of Britain's armed forces and involved elements of the RAF's strategic deterrent force — the newly-formed Valiant V-Bomber squadrons — in a limited war situation, albeit in the conventional bombing role.

By the end of 1956, the thinking in UK Government at senior level was to persuade Britain's NATO allies that nuclear deterrence was the most important factor of all in shaping a revised defence policy. What was required was a new NATO strategic concept, based on nuclear deterrence at various levels, which would enable cuts to be made in conventional force levels within the Alliance. In the RAF's case, this meant major cuts in the strength of 2nd Tactical Air Force, whose first-line squadrons were then re-equipping with the Hawker Hunter jet fighter and the English Electric Canberra light jet bomber. It was envisaged that 2 TAF's strength would be cut to one-third of its existing level of 400 aircraft; the revised force would be composed entirely of bombers and reconnaissance aircraft, with no fighters and no helicopters for army support. In other areas, Fighter Command would be reduced from 500 to 200 aircraft with the introduction of surface-to-air missiles (the Bloodhound Mk 1), while Coastal Command's strength would fall from seventy to thirty-six aircraft, equipping six squadrons. Even the V-Force, the cornerstone of Britain's deterrent policy, would not escape the constraints of economy; its planned total of 200 aircraft — Valiants, Vulcans and Victors — would be cut to 120, and perhaps 100. In the event, as a result of the findings of a Policy Review Committee at the end of 1956, the strength of the V-Force was set at 184 aircraft. However, this did not preclude future reductions in the strength of the V-Force once Blue Streak, the projected all-British Intermediate Range Ballistic Missile (IRBM) was deployed.

These reductions were totally opposed by the RAF Air Staff and in particular by the CAS, Air Chief Marshal Sir Dermot Boyle, who had the foresight to realise that once the USSR had achieved parity in the deployment of strategic nuclear weapons systems, there would be a real risk of conventional war in Europe. Yet the situation appeared to take an even gloomier turn when the Rt Hon Harold Macmillan took office as Prime Minister in January 1957; one of his first actions, having selected the Rt Hon Duncan Sandys as his Minister of Defence, was to give the latter a directive requiring him, as his first task, 'to formulate in the light of present strategic needs a new defence policy which will secure a substantial reduction in expenditure and manpower.'

For the Royal Air Force, and also for the British military aircraft industry as a whole, that one sentence signalled the beginning of twenty years of uncertainty and indecision. Yet it would be unjust to lay the blame for all the misfortunes that were to bedevil the Service over those years on the shoulders of Sandys and Macmillan; a great many politicians, often as the result of faulty and ill-advised counsel, were to make the wrong decision at the wrong time.

One of Duncan Sandys' first targets was air defence. In March 1957 — a month before that year's Defence White Paper was issued — he cancelled all work on Operational Requirement (OR) 329,

Fondly remembered by many are the days of the Vulcan force. These aircraft frequently deployed to airfields around the country.. Photographed on the Operational Readiness Platform (ORP) at RAF Wyton are three Vulcan B2s of 44 Squadron, normally based at Waddington. *(Robbie Shaw)*

which was written around an all-weather interceptor to succeed the English Electric Lightning. There were two contenders for this: the Hawker P.1121 strike and air superiority aircraft, and a combat derivative of the Fairey Delta Two (FD.2), which had briefly captured the World Air Speed Record for Britain in 1956. Work on the P.1121 continued for some months, the prototype being partially built; in 1958 the design was modified and submitted as a contender for another operational requirement, OR.339, which called for a new tactical strike and reconnaissance aircraft. This requirement was eventually met by a design submitted by a consortium of Vickers and English Electric, the TSR-2, of which more later.

The demise of OR.329 meant that the Lightning, in all probability, would be the last fighter of indigenous design to see RAF service. The Air Staff envisaged that it would equip a force of twenty squadrons, the early Lightning Mk 1 to be replaced by the more powerful Mk 3, armed first with Firestreak and then Red Top air-to-air missiles. The Lightning Force would be supported by some 700 Bloodhound SAMs.

The argument for this substantial air defence force — the development of which, it was estimated, would cost more between 1957 and 1962 than would be spent on Bomber Command — was that the manned bomber would remain the principal air threat to the United Kingdom. In 1957, the Air Staff and the Joint Intelligence Committee assessed the air threat, up to 1960, at some 300 Tu-16 Badger medium bombers backed up by a large nuclear stockpile; after 1960, the USSR would also have the capability to deploy IRBMs, but it would still require manned bombers to hit targets accurately. It was thought that, by the mid-1960s, the Russians would be technologically advanced enough to bring a new bomber into service: an aircraft capable of cruising at 1.7M, with an over-the-target dash capability of 2.0M at 60,000 feet, and a combat radius of 3,500 miles with flight refuelling. (The factual basis for such an assessment is a mystery; it has taken the Russians thirty years to produce such an aircraft, in the Blackjack strategic bomber.)

In any event, Macmillan and Sandys appear to have been sceptical. In August 1957, the Prime Minister directed Sandys to analyse the threat over the next ten years, the plans for meeting it, and the military arguments on which both were based. In fact, it was not until 1960 — after Sandys had been succeeded by the Rt Hon George Watkinson — that the size and equipment of the UK air defence was determined, and it was now based on a more realistic appraisal of the threat. Sandys, believing that the Russians would not attack Britain unless they could knock out the US deterrent at the same time, had argued that such an attack would not be possible until at least the mid-1960s, and then it would be made by missiles against which fighter aircraft were no defence. This view was shared in 1960 by the Joint Planning Staff, but not to the extent of accepting the massive reduction in fighter strength proposed by the Government. However, economic considerations once more dictated the course of events; the planned Lightning Force was reduced to five squadrons, and there were to be no SAM defences after Bloodhound Mk 1 was withdrawn in 1961. (In fact, this was later rescinded; development work continued on Bloodhound Mk 2, which had an export potential, and this was deployed as part of the UK air defence system in 1964.)

Returning to 1957, Duncan Sandys was adamant that priority was to be given to the nuclear deterrent in the shape of the V-Force, but he could not wholly defend the front line total of 184 aircraft which the Air Council planned. At a meeting of the Defence Committee in August 1957, a compromise total of 144 aircraft was reached; of these, 102 would be Mk 2 Vulcans and Victors, the remainder being the older Valiants. The Air Staff were not too disappointed, as the Mk 2 versions of the Vulcan and Victor were the crucial element; they were to be equipped with a stand-off missile, the Blue Steel, which was to carry a nuclear warhead and which would keep the airborne deterrent credible until well into the 1960s.

The Blue Streak IRBM was still very much on the agenda as part of the planned deterrent, but its development was protracted and it could not hope to be in service until well into the 1960s, and there were growing fears that by the time it became operational it would be obsolete. It was a liquid-fuel missile, requiring time to fuel and defuel, and as such it was a vulnerable system; the Americans, while hastening the deployment of their own generation of liquid-fuel ICBMs and IRBMs, were known to be giving high priority to the development of a fast-reacting, solid fuel ICBM for the next generation. (This would emerge as the Minuteman.) The alternative, for Britain, was to deploy a stop-gap missile until Blue Streak — or perhaps a solid fuel weapon — became available, and the most likely choice was the American Thor, the first examples of which had been delivered to the USAF in October 1956. In fact, the possibility of deploying the weapon in Britain was first discussed about that time, and an agreement in principle was reached between President Eisenhower and Mr Macmillan in March 1957.

In February 1958 a joint government agreement was signed under which sixty Thors were to be supplied to Britain, with twenty re-formed RAF squadrons operating three missiles each. The US Third Air Force was to assist in the construction of the Thor sites and deliver the missiles to the RAF, which would maintain and control them, while targeting was to be a matter of joint operational policy, relying on the close liaison established between the US Strategic Air Command and RAF Bomber Command. The first RAF Thor squadron (No 77) re-formed at RAF Feltwell in Norfolk on 1 September 1958, and all twenty squadrons were operational by the end of the following year. The Thor deployment in the UK ended in 1963, by which time the USAF had deployed its Atlas ICBM in the continental USA and the RAF's V-Force had achieved initial operating capability (IOC) with the Blue Steel stand-off missile. It should be mentioned that, with Thor on the point of deployment in the UK, the possibility was raised of substituting it for Blue Streak, fitting it with a warhead developed in the UK and placing it in hardened underground silos to reduce its vulnerability. In 1960, however, Blue Streak itself was cancelled, and UK deterrent policy turned towards an air-launched IRBM.

In March 1960, as the result of a meeting between Harold Macmillan and President Eisenhower, a Memorandum of Agreement was reached under which the RAF would acquire the Douglas XGAM-87A Skybolt air-launched IRBM, which had a range of just over 1,000 miles. The Vulcan B2, carrying two Skybolts initially but with the possibility of extending this capability to four or even six missiles per aircraft, would pioneer the weapon's entry into RAF service some time after 1963, when it was to start equipping the B-52 force of Strategic Air Command. The missile would have a British warhead, so preserving the autonomy of the British deterrent.

It appeared that the Skybolt programme would be a successful venture. In January 1961 a Vulcan flew to the USA to carry out electrical compatability and other trials, and in November that year another Vulcan flew in the UK with two dummy Skybolt rounds under its wings. In December, Vulcans made four dummy Skybolt drops, all from 45,000 feet at a speed of 0.84M.

The problems started in 1962, by which time a British Joint Trials Force had been formed at Eglin AFB. Five live Skybolt launches from a B-52 all ended in total or partial failure. The whole Skybolt development programme now came under review by US Secretary of Defense Robert McNamara, who was having serious doubts about it. The original idea behind Skybolt was that it would form one point of a US strategic missile triad, the other two being the land-based Minuteman and the submarine-launched Polaris. McNamara's growing opinion, in view of the latest information on the numbers of strategic missiles the Russians had at their disposal, was that Polaris and Minuteman were sufficient to counter any threat, and that therefore Skybolt was unnecessary. On 7 November 1962, McNamara recommended the President John F. Kennedy that Skybolt be cancelled.

There is little doubt that McNamara was right, from the American point of view. Polaris was already operational, and Minuteman was about to become so. The decision to cancel Skybolt was made purely on technical and cost-effective grounds, and not, as some British circles were at pains to point out, because President Kennedy had no real liking for the British and no longer wished Britain to have her own independent deterrent. This idea was nonsense; in 1962 Britain already had a deterrent, or was about to have one in the operational sense, in the form of Blue Steel. The trouble was that the cancellation of Skybolt meant that there was nothing to come after Blue Steel.

For Britain to bear the cost of Skybolt development alone was out of the question. In the end, Macmillan opted for the submarine-borne Polaris, on terms as favourable as he could get, having also rejected an American offer of the turbojet-powered Hound Dog as an alternative missile system for the V-Force. Skybolt, which had cost Britain £27 million, was dead, and so was the future of the British airborne nuclear deterrent. The Royal Navy would assume the UK deterrent role from the late 1960s; until the Polaris-equipped submarines became operational the airborne deterrent would remain in force, consisting of three squadrons of Vulcans and two of Victors, all armed with Blue Steel and depending on Quick Reaction Alert (QRA) rather than on any need to maintain a continuous airborne alert force. When they relinquished their QRA role, the Victors would be withdrawn as bombers and some converted to tankers; the Vulcan Force would be assigned to NATO in the tactical bombing role for the remainder of its fatigue life.

As far as Coastal Command was concerned, the Duncan Sandys era found the Air Ministry fighting hard to keep Maritime Air under its control. Sandys had been in favour of transferring Coastal Command to the Admiralty as early as 1954, and in November 1958 he ordered the possibility to be reappraised. The argument lasted until the following July, with the Chiefs of Staff evenly split on the question. Then Sandys changed his mind, for a reason that remains unclear; one source suggests that the Prime Minister sent Sandys a private minute in which he suggested that the issue of Coastal Command's transfer should not be raised before the forthcoming General Election, which was to take place in October 1959. What-ever the reason, Sandys issued a directive which stated that Coastal Command would continue as a separate Royal Air Force Command.

The Air Ministry at once initiated a programme to update the Avro Shackleton maritime patrol aircraft, and in 1963 issued OR.357, calling for a new maritime aircraft to succeed the Shackleton. It was to have three or more engines, jet or turboprop, and be capable of a transit to the operational area at a speed of at least 400 knots, followed by eight hours on station. After following a tortuous path, the OR eventually resulted in the Hawker Siddeley Nimrod, which was basically a Comet 4C airframe married to a weapons bay, fitted with detection systems and powered by four Rolls-Royce Spey engines.

The question of the Transport Force revolved around the needs of the Army, and in particular the rapid reinforcement of over-seas garrisons following planned reductions in manpower when National Service ended. The Suez Emergency of 1956 had shown Transport Command's resources to be woefully inadequate, and in 1957 the War Office presented Duncan Sandys with demands for a new long-range freighter, tactical transport and short-range trans-port, the latter requirement to include helicopters. At this time the workhorse of Transport Command was still the Handley Page Hastings, with three squadrons of Blackburn Beverley aircraft providing a heavy transport force and the Vickers Valetta used for short and medium haul work. Far East reinforcement was the task of one jet-equipped squadron (No. 216) with Comet C.2s. Two more squadrons earmarked mainly for Far East reinforcement were due to re-equip with twenty Bristol Britannia turboprop-powered transports, but industrial and technical difficulties, coupled with a lack of orders for the civil version, meant that production was very slow. (The first Britannia squadron, in fact, did not re-equip until the summer of 1959.)

The biggest demand confronting Mr Sandys was for a new strategic freighter, capable of carrying up to thirteen tons over a range of 3,000 miles. This co-incided with studies for a Beverley replacement; the Lockheed C-130 Hercules, which had just entered service with the USAF, was considered but then rejected on the grounds that it was too small to meet the strategic requirement and too large for a tactical transport. Besides, it was American, which did not fit in with the policy of purchasing British equipment. So, in 1958, various British alternatives were considered. They included a modified version of the Beverley, a freighter version of the Vickers VC-10, a re-designed Britannia with rear-loading doors, a new jet freighter design, the Handley Page HP111 — which was based on the Victor — and a large turboprop freighter, the Britannic, which was being developed by Shorts of Belfast.

In 1959, the issue was decided purely on political and industrial grounds. Shorts had been building Britannia components under contract, but production was almost at an end and, without the Britannic, there was no major follow-on order, which meant that a large part of the work force would have to be laid off. In view of the fact that Shorts of Belfast was government-owned, this could not be allowed to happen. So the Britannic was ordered into production to meet OR.323 for the strategic freighter; it would be known as the Belfast C.1 in RAF service.

It was not the aircraft the Air Staff wanted. For one thing, it was the only RAF aircraft to use the Rolls-Royce Tyne engine, which made little sense in logistic and engineering terms; for another, it would not be in service before 1966, three years after the required date. The Vice Chief of Air Staff of the day remarked that the aircraft would be obsolete by the time it entered service, and he was right. Proving flights to the Far East showed that the aircraft had insufficient performance to clear some of the mountains it encountered on the direct route; it had to follow roundabout routes, and it took a long time to get there, which defeated the object. The proving flight to Gan, in the Indian Ocean, provoked a caustic signal from the aircraft captain to HQ Transport Command; he stated that all was well, and there was no sign of scurvy in the crew!

When the Belfast was chosen, the other War Office requirements for air transport still had to be met. The Army required sufficient aircraft to carry out a Brigade Group parachute drop; to move two Brigade Groups to an overseas theatre within a fortnight; and to assure the supply of up to six Brigade Groups during the first month of a limited war. The Army did not get all the aircraft it wanted, but the Air Council went a substantial way towards meeting the requirement; the biggest single order involved fifty Armstrong-Whitworth Argosy medium-range transports, which began to enter service in 1962, while the Comet jet transport force was augmented by a number of Comet 4Cs. The decision was also taken to equip one squadron with the Vickers VC-10. In the helicopter field, the general purpose force was augmented by additional Westland Whirlwinds, while the Westland Belvedere twin-rotor helicopter was chosen as a tactical transport, even though the Army favoured the American Boeing-Vertol Chinook. The Belvedere was a disaster; its cramped cabin made it completely unsuitable as a troop transport, it had an airframe life of only 1,600 hours and it never met its operational requirements. It entered service in 1961 and was withdrawn in 1969. In the meantime, orders had been placed for the far more reliable Westland Wessex, which began to enter RAF service in 1964.

In Nato's front line, 2nd TAF was reduced to just over 200 aircraft by March 1958. The tactical strike force comprised four squadrons of Canberras, while the PR element comprised two squadrons of Canberras and two squadrons of Swift FR.5s. Air defence rested on two squadrons of Gloster Javelin all-weather fighters and one squadron of Hawker Hunter day fighters, the remainder having disbanded in 1957-8.

In this area, the principal requirement of the late 1950s was for a Canberra replacement. 2nd TAF's Canberra strike squadrons were about to adopt a low-level nuclear bombing role involving aerobatic manoeuvres at high g — a sharp pull-up followed by a roll off the top of a loop after weapon release — and this would have an adverse effect upon their fatigue lives. In keeping with the UK Government's policy of maintaining a nuclear deterrent force at various levels, finding a replacement by the mid-1960s was imperative. Accordingly, OR.339 was issued, and from the various contenders the design tendered by the Vickers/English Electric consortium, soon to become the British Aircraft Corporation, was selected to meet it.

The choice of this new tactical strike and reconnaissance aircraft, the TSR-2 was announced on 1 January 1959. Development work went ahead at Weybridge and Warton, and a Management Board comprising representatives of the RAF, the Ministry of Aviation and BAC was set up to control the project. It was the first time in the history of British aviation that decisions affecting the design of an aircraft were taken away from the design team involved and placed in the hands of a committee, and it was to prove a very unwise decision.

At this time the Air Staff was also beginning to show an interest in another design which appeared to have great tactical potential as a replacement for the Hawker Hunter. This was the Hawker P.1127 vertical take-off project, which had been proceeding as a private venture without any form of government backing, although development of its Bristol vectored-thrust engine was proceeding with the help of US funding. In April 1959 the Air Staff issued a draft Operational Requirement, GOR 345, which was written around the project. There was also considerable interest in the idea from NATO, where a requirement existed for a new tactical fighter-bomber, although to meet this a heavier and more advanced aircraft, with supersonic and all-weather capability, would be needed.

Work on building the prototype P.1127 proceeded during 1959, and the prototype made its first tethered hovering flight in October 1960. Both the Air Staff and the Ministry of Aviation were unimpressed; neither thought that the aircraft had much combat potential. Seeing little prospect of an RAF production order at that time, Hawker turned its attention to proposals for a more advanced VTOL aircraft that would more adequately suit the NATO requirement, then emerging in draft form.

The new Hawker design, the P.1150, was to be powered by an advanced version of the Pegasus vectored-thrust engine using a new type of exhaust boost known as Plenum Chamber Burning (PCB), which involved the burning of fuel in fully oxygen-rich air and at higher pressures than in most reheat systems. However, when the firm NATO requirement — NBMR-3 — was issued, it called for a larger VTOL configuration, so the P.1150 was abandoned and replaced by a new design, the P.1154. It was to be powered by a new engine, the Bristol Siddeley BS.100, again using PCB. Then the problems started to emerge.

First of all, mainly because of France's reluctance to participate in a joint venture in bringing NBMR-3 to fruition, NATO withdrew its entire requirement. In mid-1962 the Air Staff and the Admiralty attempted to draft a joint requirement for a combat aircraft based on the P.1154, but this was doomed from the outset; the RAF wanted a single-seat low-level strike aircraft with a secondary intercept capability, while the RN needed a two-seat all-weather interceptor for aircraft carrier operations with low-level strike as a secondary requirement. The two were directly opposed to each other, and late in 1963 the Royal Navy opted out of the P.1154 programme and decided to order the Spey-powered F-4 Phantom instead. The RAF pursued the P.1154 project alone, until it was cancelled by a new Labour administration in January 1965.

The second project to be killed by the Labour Government was the Hawker Siddeley HS.681, a medium-range short take-off and landing (STOL) freighter proposed to meet Operational Requirement OR.351 in 1961. This left only the BAC TSR-2 as the British aircraft industry's only major military programme. The whole unhappy story surrounding the development of this aircraft needs no repetition here; the salient point is that research and development costs, estimated at £90 million in 1960, had doubled by the beginning of 1963, and the whole schedule had slipped by two years. By the end of 1963 the writing was already on the wall for TSR-2, although neither the government nor BAC would admit it. Escalating R and D costs had made the project the subject of heated controversy; the Labour opposition, influenced by 'advisors' who had a minimal knowledge of military aviation, and even less of the RAF's operational requirements, made political capital out of the funds that were being diverted to keep TSR-2 alive, and left the electorate in no doubt about what they would do to the project if they got into power. But there were sinister forces at work within the Ministry of Defence, too; the Chief of the Defence Staff, Lord Louis Mountbatten, made no secret of the fact that he favoured a land-based version of the Buccaneer to meet the RAF's requirement, while the Ministry's Chief Scientific Adviser, Sir Solly Zuckermann, told everyone concerned that he regarded TSR-2 as a waste of public money, and that better value could be obtained by buying equipment from the United States.

The prototype TSR-2 flew from Boscombe Down on 27 September 1964. Some problems with the undercarriage delayed the next flight until the last day of the year, but after that the test programme picked up rapidly and seven flights were made in January 1965. The aircraft went supersonic for the first time on 21 February, and high-speed low-altitude trials began in March. By this time the second prototype had also joined the flying programme, and work was progressing on a third prototype and twenty production aircraft, five of which were partly complete.

Meanwhile, the Labour Government had kept the project going so that the aircraft could be evaluated against its American rival, the General Dynamics F-111. At that time, Prime Minister Harold Wilson — acting on faulty advice — seriously believed that some £300 million might be saved by buying the American aircraft; his Cabinet thought so too, and the final nail in TSR-2's coffin was hammered home on 6 April 1965, when Chancellor James Callaghan, during his Budget speech, announced that the project was to be cancelled forthwith. The assassination was to be complete; no trace of the project was to survive. Orders were given for the destruction of the two completed prototypes and those on the assembly line, and all of the jigs and tools used by the manufacturing companies.

Who can forget the sight and sound of Lightnings climbing almost vertically out of Binbrook on exercises and actual scrambles to intercept inquisitive Soviet Bear aircraft. Landing at the Lincolnshire airfield is a Lightning F6 of 11 Squadron. *(Robbie Shaw)*

On 1 February 1966, Defence Minister Denis Healey announced that the UK Government was to purchase fifty F-111s to carry out the task for which TSR-2 had been intended. The 1966 Defence White Paper, issued later that month, stated that the F-111 would bridge the gap between 1970, when the Canberra 'could not safely continue' in the strike and reconnaissance roles, and the mid-1970s, when an Anglo-French Variable Geometry Aircraft would begin to take over these roles. The latter project had been initiated in May 1965, when a Memorandum of Understanding had been signed by representatives of the British and French Governments. The AFVG prototype was expected to fly in 1971 or 1972, with first deliveries to the RAF being made in 1974. For the RAF, the AFVG was envisaged primarily as a strike/reconnaissance aircraft, with the secondary role of interception.

It has already been mentioned that the Royal Navy had opted for the McDonnell F-4 Phantom instead of the problematical P.1154. The intention to buy this aircraft was announced in February 1964 by the then Conservative Government; the original intention was to procure 130 Phantoms to replace the Sea Vixen as the standard fleet defence aircraft, but this was later reduced to fifty-two. In RN service the Phantom was to be designated F-4K Phantom FG.1.

In February 1962 McDonnell had proposed to the US forces a Phantom powered by Rolls-Royce Spey engines, and to appease the British aircraft industry the then Minister of Aviation, Roy Jenkins, announced in November 1965 that the Spey was to power the

British Phantoms. Before that, in May 1965 — following the cancellation of TSR-2 — the Phantom had also been ordered for the Royal Air Force; at this stage it was anticipated that the total RN/RAF procurement would be some 290 aircraft. The RAF Phantom was to be designated F-4M, and in-service date was set for 1968.

The Phantom was to replace the Canberra and Hunter in the reconnaissance and strike roles, and would carry out these tasks until the advent of a more specialized tactical strike and reconnaissance aircraft. This was to be another Anglo-French project, the Breguet/BAC Jaguar; a Memorandum of Understanding covering the development of this aircraft was signed on 17 May 1965 between the UK and French Defence Ministers. When the Jaguar entered RAF service in the early 1970s, some of the Phantoms would be released from tactical duties and would replace part of the Lightning Force in the air defence role.

The 1966 Defence White Paper made no mention of a firm order for the Hawker P.1127, although an Air Staff Requirement, ASR.384, had been issued in the spring of 1965, calling for an RAF development of this aircraft. Six pre-production aircraft were ordered in 1965, the first of these flying in August 1966, but it was not until early in 1967 that Hawker Siddeley received a contract for sixty production aircraft, to be named the Harrier GR.Mk. 1. The Harrier was to equip, initially, one tactical support squadron in the UK and another in Germany, as well as a Harrier Conversion Unit. It was a cautious commitment, but it was a first step along the V/STOL road which, in the future, was to prove of inestimable value to Britain's defences.

For Transport Command, the aircraft which had been selected to fill the void left by the cancelled HS.681 project was the Lockheed C-130K Hercules. Sixty-six of these were on order, and the first flew in 1966. That year's Defence White Paper also mentioned that there was now 'a firm production commitment' for the Hawker Siddeley 801, which was to replace the Shackleton and which was to enter service 'at the end of the 1960s'.

The 1966 Defence White Paper left its readers in no doubt about one issue: the Anglo-French VG aircraft was to be the very core of Britain's future air defence and military aircraft industry programmes. Powered by a very advanced engine, the M.45, developed jointly by Bristol Siddeley and SNECMA, it was to be a two-seater with a maximum speed of 800 knots at sea level and 2.5M at altitude; operational ceiling was to be better than 60,000 feet, and combat radius 500 nautical miles. However, the project was dogged by problems from the very start, not least of which was that the British and French operational requirements were incompatible with one another. In the summer of 1967, on the grounds of cost, the French Government announced its intention to withdraw from the AFVG programme. The decision threw the British Government into complete confusion. Rather lamely, Defence Minister Healey announced that urgent consideration was being given to the new situation, and that while investigating the possibility of collaboration with other countries the Government was authorising British firms to carry out a project study on a VG aircraft to a modified specification.

That was the first blow to strike at the Labour administration's future plans for the RAF. The second came very swiftly thereafter, when it was realised that the planned purchase of fifty F-111s could not possibly be supported due to wildly escalating costs. The excuse for its cancellation, given in January 1968, was that with the progressive withdrawal of British forces from the Far East and the Arabian Gulf by 1971, there would no longer be a need for a long-range tactical strike and reconnaissance aircraft. So the F-111 order was cancelled, at a cost of some £50 million. Those in power apparently ignored the fact that, with reductions in overseas force levels making rapid deployment necessary in the event of an emergency, the need for such an aircraft would be even more imperative.

In the course of 1968 the Royal Air Force underwent a major reorganisation. On the last day of April, Fighter and Bomber Commands merged to become Strike Command. In 1969, Coastal and Signals Commands disbanded and also became an integrated part of Strike Command, being re-designated Nos. 18 (Maritime) and 90 (Signals) Groups respectively. Flying Training and Technical Training Commands also merged, on 1 June 1968, to become Training Command. Air Support Command, as Transport Command had been re-named in 1967, remained an autonomous Command until 1 September 1972, when it too merged with Strike Command to complete the formation of a single UK operational command. A new Group, No. 46, was formed to control and direct the long-range transport forces, while No. 38 Group provided offensive support for forces in the field.

In 1969 the RAF at last began to receive some of the new equipment which had been ordered in the wake of the 1965 cancellations. On 7 May the first Phantom FGR Mk 2 squadron, No. 6 Squadron, formed at RAF Coningsby in Lincolnshire as an offensive air support unit within No. 38 Group, while the first Phantom air defence unit, No. 43 Squadron, formed at RAF Leuchars on 1 September. This squadron was equipped with Phantom FG.1s, ex-Royal Navy aircraft which had been relinquished with the phasing out of the RN's fleet carriers.

On 1 October 1969 the first Harrier squadron — No. 1 Squadron at RAF Wittering, and the first Buccaneer squadron — No. 12 Squadron at RAF Honington, both formed. The Buccaneer S.Mk. 2 had been transferred to the RAF from the Royal Navy, again as the result of the latter relinquishing much of its fixed-wing combat force, to provide a mobile nuclear-capable strike force to bridge the gap left by the demise of the F-111. Also in October, the first Hawker Siddeley Nimrod entered service with the Maritime Operational Training Unit at RAF St Mawgan, in Cornwall.

Re-equipment continued during the early 1970s, years that saw more sweeping changes affecting the Royal Air Force. In November 1971 the Far East Air Force disbanded, although the RAF continued to maintain a small force of Nimrod MR aircraft, on a rotational basis, and a squadron of helicopters in Singapore as part of a five-power defence force. The RAF's contribution was supplemented by frequent visits of Vulcans, Buccaneers and Phantoms. These deployments were greatly assisted by flight refuelling, using the Handley Page Victor K.1As (and later K.2s) of the Marham Tanker Wing. In December 1971 the RAF also completed its withdrawal from the Arabian Gulf, leaving no permanent presence east of Suez with the exception of a single helicopter squadron in Hong Kong.

This reduced the RAF to two overseas Commands, the Near East Air Force and RAF Germany. In the case of NEAF, following the British withdrawal from Libya, the RAF was concentrated on two islands, Malta and Cyprus, although the Command also had responsibility for the staging posts at Masirah — the only presence to be retained in the Gulf — and the airfield at Salalah, in the Dhofar region of Oman. By the late 1970s, the RAF was to withdraw from Malta, too.

HQ Near East Air Force disbanded on 31 March 1976, and British Forces Cyprus formed on the following day, with AHQ Cyprus as a subordinate command under the control of RAF Strike Command. AHQ Cyprus disbanded early in 1988, whereupon activities at RAF Akrotiri were administered directly by HQ Strike Command in the United Kingdom.

By the 1970s, the United Kingdom's membership of NATO had become paramount in the nation's defence policy, and Britain's contribution to the Atlantic Alliance was without question the first priority. The RAF was also assuming full responsibility for the provision of strike/reconnaissance and air defence forces for the Fleet, as the Royal Navy's aircraft carriers were phased out. (Much of that burden was to be alleviated in the 1980s, when the Royal Navy deployed its Sea Harrier squadrons.) At the same time, the United Kingdom was to retain certain residual responsibilities outside Europe — commitments to Britain's remaining dependent territories overseas, for example, and certain responsibilities within the Commonwealth and to the United Nations — and so the Royal Air Force was required to retain a general capability for operations outside Europe. The forces and their equipment which might be used for such operations were to be drawn from resources in the European Theatre.

In May 1973 the first of the Anglo-French Jaguar GR.1 tactical strike aircraft was delivered to the newly-created Jaguar OCU at RAF Lossiemouth. In March 1974 No. 54 Squadron also began equipping with the Jaguar, and was followed by No. 6 Squadron later in the year. These two squadrons formed the tactical strike element of No. 38 Group, and were joined in 1976 by No. 41 Squadron, operating in the tactical reconnaissance role. By the summer of 1977 four tactical strike and one PR squadrons in Germany had also re-equipped with the Jaguar. (One of these, No. 20, had been operating Harrier GR.1s since 1970; the rest had been operating the Phantom FGR.2.)

The advent of the Jaguar meant that, in terms of aircraft, the equivalent of seven squadrons of Phantoms could now be re-assigned to the air defence role, replacing the Lightning. Phantoms were allocated to the Gütersloh Wing (Nos. 19 and 92 Squadrons) for the air defence of 2nd ATAF, and to Nos. 23, 29, 56 and 111 Squadrons for the air defence of the United Kingdom. They also equipped the air combat element of No. 228 OCU, which bore the shadow identity of No. 64 Squadron. This left only two squadrons, Nos. 5 and 11 at RAF Binbrook, still equipped with the Lightning.

The RAF's principal tactical strike and reconnaissance aircraft, then, was the Jaguar, which was to remain in this role until eventually replaced by the forthcoming Anglo-German-Italian Multi-Role Combat Aircraft, which had arisen out of the ashes of the AFVG and which was to become the Tornado. (Its development story is told in the section on RAF Strike Command.) For overland interdiction there were two squadrons of Buccaneers in Germany, Nos. 15 and 16, with two more — Nos. 12 and 208 — in the UK, supported by the Buccaneer OCU. The Buccaneer squadrons in Germany would also be replaced by the Tornado in due course, while those in the UK would be retained in the anti-shipping role.

Close fixed-wing support for the Army in Germany, now that No. 20 Squadron had converted to Jaguars, rested on Nos. 3 and 4 Squadrons, with the Harrier. Also with Harriers in the UK was No. 1 Squadron, plus the Harrier OCU.

For maritime reconnaissance, in the late 1970s, there were four squadrons of Nimrod MR.Mk. 1s: Nos. 120, 201 and 206 Squadrons at RAF Kinloss, and No. 42 Squadron, plus the Nimrod OCU, at RAF St Mawgan. A fifth Nimrod squadron, No. 203, which had been based on Malta, disbanded in December 1977 as the British forces withdrew from the island, its aircraft assets being divided between the other squadrons or allocated for development work.

The remainder of the V-Force, comprising the Vulcan B.2s of No. 1 Group Strike Command, was divided between RAF Scampton and RAF Waddington, awaiting disbandment once the Tornado began to enter service. The pooled Vulcan resources of Nos. 44, 50 and 101 Squadrons were at RAF Waddington, still assigned to SACEUR in the free-fall bombing role, while Nos. 27, 35 and 617 Squadrons were at RAF Scampton, together with the Vulcan OCU. Of these, No. 27 Squadron was operating in the Maritime Radar Reconnaissance role with modified Vulcan B.2s (MRR). The other type which had helped to sustain the RAF's airborne deterrent force during the 1960s, the Handley Page Victor, continued to operate in the K.2 tanker version, equipping Nos. 55 and 57 Squadrons had No. 232 OCU at RAF Marham; the primary function of these squadrons was to extend the effective radius of the UK air defences, refuelling Phantoms and Lightnings on QRA.

The Hercules Tactical Transport Force, which had comprised six squadrons at its peak in the early 1970s, was now reduced to four with the disbandment, in 1975 and 1976, of Nos. 36 and 48 Squadrons. The long-range transport element had also been reduced with the disbandment of No. 216 Squadron (Comet C.4s) in 1975, followed by Nos. 99 and 511 Squadrons (Britannias) and No. 53 Squadron (Belfasts) in 1976. This left the RAF with one fast long-range transport unit, No. 10 Squadron, operating VC-10s. The tactical helicopter force comprised three squadrons of Westland Wessex, one of which was in Hong Kong, and two squadrons of

Westland/Aerospatiale Pumas. Thirty-three Chinook heavy-lift helicopters were on order, delivery to begin in 1980.

Flying training in the RAF was still carried out on the Jet Provost T.3A and T.5A, which equipped four flying training schools, the Central Flying School and the RAF College, Cranwell. Advanced flying training with No. 4 FTS at Valley, Anglesey, which had used the Hunter T.7 for many years, was now carried out on the British Aerospace Hawk T.1. Two Tactical Weapons Units continued to operate the Hunter, but these too were scheduled to re-equip fully with the Hawk early in 1980s.

The overall picture presented by the Royal Air Force at the dawn of a new decade, therefore, was of a Service greatly reduced in size and level of commitments around the world. At the same time, it was a Service making a vital contribution to NATO, and therefore to the security of the Free World, and with the advent of the Tornado in the 1980s that contribution would grow enormously. Moreover, existing equipment, such as the Nimrod, was being updated to extend its useful life into the 1990s.

In 1980, no-one could have foreseen that within two years, the RAF would be taking part in a limited but deadly conflict which, in a few weeks of operations, would reveal or confirm a number of serious shortcomings in equipment and procedures. The first such shortfall revealed by the Falklands War of May-June 1982 was the limitations of the relatively small tanker force in sustaining large-scale air operations a long way from home base, a problem made more complex by the fact key aircraft engaged in the operations (Vulcan, Nimrod and Hercules) were not equipped for air-to-air refuelling at the outset and consequently had to be modified hastily, and their crews trained or refreshed in the appropriate techniques, at very short notice.

The second, and far more costly, shortfall was the complete lack of airborne early warning coverage for the Fleet. In the NATO/UK environment AEW was the responsibility of the Royal Air Force, or more specifically of No. 8 Squadron, which was operating elderly Shackleton AEW.2 aircraft in this role with a promise of more advanced AEW aircraft just around the corner. After the Falklands conflict the question of providing effective AEW coverage for the Royal Navy assumed urgent priority, and although it was solved to some extent by helicopter-borne AEW systems, the RAF's AEW requirement was beset by a series of complex and expensive pitfalls, as we shall see in due course.

The third point to emerge from the Falklands War — and probably the most important of all, as far as future RAF/RN operations are concerned — is that it could not have been won without the V/STOL Harrier. V/STOL was a key factor then; it is a recipe for survival, and will remain so for the future.

The Falklands War, more than any other event of the past twenty-five years, has influenced the RAF's operational procedures as they are today, and will be tomorrow. The purpose of this book is to examine them in detail, and to discuss the adequacy of the equipment with which the Royal Air Force must perform its operational tasks.

# CHAPTER ONE

## No. 1 Group, Strike Command

From its HQ at RAF Upavon, in Wiltshire, No. 1 Group RAF Strike Command exercises control over the RAF's strike/attack, tanker and transport forces. Its principal strike/attack aircraft is the Panavia Tornado GR.1, which equips the Tornado Weapons Conversion Unit and No. 13 Squadron at RAF Honington in Suffolk, Nos. 27 and 617 Squadrons at RAF Marham in Norfolk, and the Trinational Tornado Training Establishment at RAF Cottesmore in Leicestershire. This was the first Tornado establishment to open, in January 1981, and within two years had reached a peak complement of fifty aircraft — twenty-two German, twenty-one British, and seven Italian. The TWCU at Honington was formed when the TTTE had reached an interim complement of forty Tornados.

The variable-geometry Tornado is the result of a 1960s requirement for a strike and reconnaissance aircraft capable of carrying a heavy and varied weapons load and of penetrating foreseeable Warsaw Pact defensive systems by day and night and in all weathers. It would have to be endowed with an excellent low-level performance and be capable of hitting a pinpoint target, such as a bridge, in a single pass, for which it would need to be equipped with the most advanced avionics. It must also be able to carry out tactical reconnaissance, and have the potential to be developed into an interceptor.

In time of tension the aircraft and personnel of the Tornado Weapons Conversion Unit (TWCU) would form No. 45 Squadron. That unit's markings are carried on the aircraft's nose. *(Robbie Shaw)*

The original solution to the requirement was the British Aircraft Corporation (formerly English Electric) TSR-2, which was cancelled, mainly as a consequence of political mismanagement, in 1965. In the following year an Anglo-French Variable Geometry Aircraft (AFVG) was proposed, but in July 1967, again as a result of political intrigue, France pulled out of the project. In the meantime, the German Federal Republic, in collaboration with the United States, had been pursuing studies of an advanced VTOL strike aircraft, but this too was cancelled in January 1968. A few days later the British Government announced that, as part of extensive defence cuts, it was to cancel an order for fifty General Dynamics F-111 aircraft which it had intended to purchase from the United States to fill the strike/reconnaissance gap. Instead, the requirement would be met by several squadrons of Buccaneer S.Mk. 2s which would serve as an 'acceptable substitute' until an entirely new aircraft could be brought into service.

Meanwhile, the British Aircraft Corporation had been pursuing design studies of an all-British variable geometry combat aircraft,

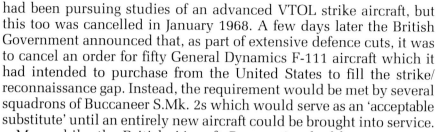

Below: You can almost feel the concentration as the pilot of this Tornado GR1 plugs into the hose of the VC-10 tanker.
*(Robbie Shaw)*

the UKVG, while discussions went on with Belgium, Canada, Germany, Italy and the Netherlands on the possibility of collaboration in the development of a multi-role combat aircraft for service in 1975. Eventually the participants were reduced to Britain, Germany and Italy, and these three nations were left to set up the machinery that would bring the MRCA to fruition. A consortium of companies was formed under the name of Panavia; it consisted principally of the British Aircraft Corporation (later British Aerospace), Messerschmitt-Bölkow-Blohm (MBB) and Aeritalia, together with many sub-contractors. The baseline aircraft was drawn up in March 1969, and in May the three nations concerned signed a Memorandum of Understanding (MoU) on the definition phase. Four months later the Rolls-Royce RB-199 turbofan was selected as the new aircraft's powerplant, and a new engine company, Turbo-Union, was formed by Rolls-Royce, MTU of Germany and Fiat.

The collaborative road was often steep and rocky, dogged in places by German funding difficulties, the length of time taken to reach joint

Above: An RAF Tornado GR1 of the Tri-national Tornado Training Establishment (TTTE) at its Cottesmore base.
*(Robbie Shaw)*

decisions, and — in Britain's case — a damaging engineers' strike at British Aerospace in 1979. Most of these troubles came later in the programme, however, and had nothing to do with the concept of the aircraft itself. In the early stages, one of the biggest obstacles was Germany's requirement for a single-seat variant, but this was dropped in March 1970 and this enabled the definition phase to be completed in the following month. By this time the MRCA had been adopted as a NATO programme (in November 1969), and in July 1970 Britain and Germany signed an MoU to launch development, Italy joining the development programme on an official basis in October.

The first of nine Tornado IDS (Interdictor/Strike) prototypes flew in Germany on 14 August 1974, the second flying from Warton in Lancashire shortly afterwards. By this time the roles the aircraft was to undertake in RAF service were clearly defined. They were nuclear strike, counter-air (airfield attack), interdiction, close air support, tactical reconnaissance and maritime strike. The aircraft would remain constant for these varying missions; only the weapons fit would change.

The first RAF Tornado GR.1s were delivered to RAF Cottesmore in July 1980, the TTTE being formed there in January 1981 for the purpose of training the crews of all three participant countries. There were — and are — six principal training tasks, as follows:

1. Preparing and planning a sortie to include simulated weapons aiming and release.
2. Navigating to, and carrying out low-level simulated attacks on, one or more targets.
3. Carrying out simulated low-level attacks against a mobile 'radar bomb score unit' target.
4. Recognition of electronic warfare threats.
5. Planning and executing escape manoeuvres after an attack.
6. Taking evasive action against an air attack without detracting from the main task.

A Tornado GR1 of the TWCU shows its 'all weather' capability as it begins its take-off run from a semi-flooded Honington runway. *(Robbie Shaw)*

All Tornados at the TTTE have a war role, providing a large and useful back-up force for the front-line squadrons. So have the aircraft at the TWCU, Honington, which carries the 'shadow' designation of No. 45 Squadron. The TWCU began operations in January 1982 and has an establishment of twenty-two aircraft, its primary task being to introduce crews fresh from the TTTE to the weapons and operational use of the Tornado GR.1 and to develop their tactical flying. The TWCU also runs a weapons instructor course to give extra flying and ground schooling to experienced pilots. Also at Honington is the Tornado Standards Unit, which ensures that standards and procedures are maintained on the type throughout the RAF and which monitors the content of the training courses.

Top (left): Loaded with long range fuel tanks, practice bombs and Skyshadow ECM pods, this Tornado GR1 of 27 Squadron was photographed high above the clouds over the North Sea. *(Robbie Shaw)*
Above (left): The second Tornado reconnaissance squadron is No 13, based at Honington. This photograph of their first aircraft was taken soon after delivery to the squadron. *(Robbie Shaw)*
Opposite: In full afterburner, a Tornado GR1 of 617 'Dambusters' Squadron departs CFB Baden-Sollingen where it was deployed to participate in the NATO Tactical Air Meet of 1988. *(Robbie Shaw)*

Below (left): The graceful lines of the Victor belie its age. The sole operator of the type is 55 Squadron at Marham, and one of the unit's aircraft is illustrated with all three hoses trailing. *(Robbie Shaw)*
Bottom (left): No. 101 Squadron operates both the K2 (foreground) and K3 (background) variants of the VC-10 from Brize Norton. *(Robbie Shaw)*

Aside from tactical nuclear weapons — the British WE177 tactical nuclear bomb — the Tornado GR.1 carries several types of offensive conventional armament. Its total weapons load is 16,000 lb, which can include eight Mk. 83 1,000 lb 'iron bombs' under the fuselage, but one of the most effective weapons in its armoury is the Hunting Engineering JP233 airfield attack weapon system, which comprises two disposable airborne dispensers — the first housing thirty SG357 cratering submunitions and the second 215 HB876 area denial mines.

In a normal airfield attack the Tornado would carry two JP233s and dispense its total load in a single pass across or along the target runway. This would produce a line of craters overlaid by a minefield, so destroying the runway and denying access to crater repair personnel. The aircraft is also compatible with the BL755 cluster bomb, which is primarily an anti-armour weapon, the Paveway laser-guided bomb, AS-30 ASM, Maverick, GBU-15, Sea Eagle and Kormoran anti-shipping missiles, napalm, 'smart' and retarded bombs, BLU-1B 750 lb fire bombs, Matra 500 lb ballistic and retarded bombs, Lepus flare bombs, LAU-51A and LR-25 rocket launchers, active and passive ECM pods, Pave Spike pods, data link pods and chaff/flare dispensers.

The Tornado GR.1, which is powered by two Turbo-Union RB-199-34R Mk. 101 turbofans, each rated at 9,000 lb st dry and 16,000 lb st with reheat, has an impressive array of avionics to enable it to carry out its mission. At the heart of the system is the Central Digital Computer, which calculates the aircraft's present position from four sources: the Ferranti FIN 1010 three-axis digital inertial navigation system (DINS) which provides primary heading, attitude and velocity; a twin-gyro platform (SAHR) to give secondary heading and attitude; a Decca Type 72 Doppler radar system providing secondary velocity; and a Microtecnica air data computer (ADC) which supplies data such as true airspeed and Mach number.

The information is passed from computer to crew through several channels. In the front cockpit, the pilot's primary reference sourse is the Smiths/Teldix/OMI head-up display; he also has a GEC Avionics/Aeritalia autopilot and flight director which uses two self-monitoring computers, a GEC/Bodenseewerk triplex command stability augmentation system, a Ferranti projected map display, a GEC terrain-following E-scope display, a Texas Instruments terrain-following radar and a Smiths Industries horizontal situation indicator.

With the aid of its large brake parachute, this Victor K2 of 55 Squadron decelerates after landing on Scampton's wet runway. *(Robbie Shaw)*

In the rear cockpit, the navigator's avionics equipment includes a TV tabular display produced by GEC in partnership with AEG and Selenia, a Ferranti Comed combined radar and projected map display, navigation mode panel, Texas Instruments ground mapping radar, stores management system, weapon-aiming mode selector, laser ranger and marked target seeker, passive radar warning receiver and active ECM system.

Opposite: The receiver's eye view of a refuelling basket trailed from a Tristar of 216 Squadron. *(Robbie Shaw)*

The only weaponry controlled by the Tornado pilot is the built-in armament of two 27 mm Mauser cannon; the navigator, via the stores management system, controls everything else. Thanks to this system, he can assign weapons to a particular target before flight; when a release signal is received from the main computer, the stores management system automatically drops the correct selection of weapons from their hardpoints. This leaves the navigator free to monitor the progress of the flight on his ground-mapping radar and carry out position fixes and weapon aiming as necessary, while the

Below: A VC-10 K2 of 101 Squadron demonstrating its ability to refuel two fighters simultaneously. *(Robbie Shaw)*

pilot monitors the terrain-following radar. Although all sortie details are entered on a cassette, which is loaded on to the main computer — a Litef Spirit 3 64K — before flight, the crew can enter a revised flight plan into the computer at any time using either of the moving maps or TV displays. The computer, knowing the aircraft's present position and planned route, can then issue steering commands to the HUD, autopilot, horizontal situation indicator and TV displays.

No Tornado IDS replacement is at present envisaged. Instead, various mid-life improvements designed to maintain mission effectiveness into the next century are being planned by the operating countries in collaboration with industry, although it is unlikely that this will result in a programme common to all air arms. The MRCA/Tornado programme started off in the first place with the intention of developing a weapons system that would be common to the needs of the UK, Germany and Italy, but this was quickly seen to be impracticable. Even today, the operational requirements of the user air forces within NATO continue to diverge.

Above: As yet the Tristar fleet have not been fitted with wing mounted refuelling pods, and can refuel only one aircraft at a time from one of the two hoses trailed from the fuselage station. The recipient on this occasion is a 74 Squadron F-4J Phantom. *(Robbie Shaw)*

One area in which this is apparent is in the choice of an anti-radiation missile to enhance Tornado's survivability. Tornado GR.1's primary mission is to strike deep into hostile territory in order to destroy airfields and other key targets; the first line of defence is to fly low and fast, preferably under cover of night or poor weather. This is supported by electronic defences: radar warning, passive and active ECM (in the form of the Sky Shadow ECM pod that gives each Tornado its own ECM cover), and — when it is fitted as part of the proposed update — a missile warning radar.

At low altitude, under cover of darkness or low visibility, the primary threat to Tornado comes from radar-directed anti-aircraft artillery and SAMs, both fixed and mobile. For this reason, the RAF decided to equip its strike/attack Tornados with a defence suppression missile. The requirement dates back to 1977, when Air Staff Target 1228 was formulated, and by 1983 two main contenders had emerged. These were the Texas Instruments AGM-88 HARM (High Speed Anti-Radiation Missile) and the British Aerospace ALARM (Air-Launched Anti-Radar Missile). In June 1983 the MoD opted for ALARM, which was judged to be more suited to the RAF's operational tasks than HARM. The latter missile was cheaper than its British counterpart, it was faster and it would be ready for operational use much earlier, but — quite apart from the fact that British jobs and British technology were at stake—ALARM was only about half its size and it was envisaged that up to nine could be carried on a Tornado without making too many sacrifices in terms of war load, fuel or ECM equipment.

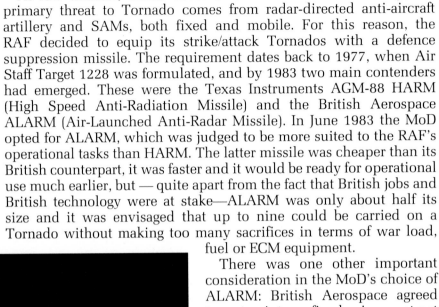

Viewed from the cockpit of a fighter, the Tristar is an awesome sight, as evident in this portrait of a Tristar K1 of 216 Squadron trailing one of its hoses. *(Robbie Shaw)*

There was one other important consideration in the MoD's choice of ALARM: British Aerospace agreed to enter into a fixed-price contract based on a run of 2,000 missiles, a high proportion of which would be for export. This effectively doubled the planned production run, enabling British Aerospace to quote the MoD a much lower unit price than had at first been envisaged. By this time, British Aerospace and Marconi Defence Systems, who were developing the missile's radar seeker, had spent more than £3 million on development work, and were confident that all complex technical problems could be overcome within the laid-down time-scale. It was envisaged that some 750 ALARMs would have been delivered to the RAF by the middle of 1989.

ALARM is intended for use in conjunction with attacks on targets whose radar defences are well documented. Before a planned attack, the weapon would be programmed on the ground with a library of radar signatures, enabling its seeker to compare and identify the signals it receives, and a list of target radars arranged in order of priority according to the threats most likely to be encountered on a particular mission. Armed with these two sets of data, ALARM can be launched without lock-on and without being tuned to a particular threat by the Tornado's radar warning receiver. During development, however, a digital databus was incorporated into the missile itself, enabling the crew to re-programme the missile in flight; an obvious advantage in the event of a change in mission priority.

ALARM's primary mode of operation is indirect attack, which would be used against a heavily-defended target. In this, the missile is launched at low level, climbs to around 40,000 feet and deploys a parachute, loitering while it searches for radar emissions. It then selects its target, according to threat priority, and dives on it unpowered at high speed. If the radar ceases to transmit, an on-board INS guidance system keeps the missile on course. The secondary mode is direct attack, in which the missile is fired towards the target with or without lock-on; if it fails to acquire a target within a pre-determined distance, it climbs to altitude, deploys its parachute and searches for another.

Testing of ALARM's sub-systems, including the Royal Ordnance-designed rocket motor, the warhead and the parachute system began in 1984, and ballasted dummy rounds were used for separation trials and to explore the effect of the weapon on aircraft handling. However, testing of the rocket motor at the Propellants,

The power of the Rolls-Royce Pegasus engine in the Harrier is evident in this shot of GR3 of 233 OCU lifting off from a rain soaked runway. *(Robbie Shaw)*

Explosives and Rocket Motor Establishment (PERME), revealed serious problems, and in the end British Aerospace switched to a new powerplant developed by a West German firm, Bayern Chemie. Flight trials were proceeding at the end of 1988, but by this time the programme had slipped by two years and it was unlikely that the weapon would be in RAF service before mid-1990. In the meantime, the US AGM-88 HARM had been selected for the Luftwaffe's Tornados, and first deliveries were made in November 1987.

The use of ALARM will be especially relevant to the war role of No. 1 Group's Tornados, which, with in-flight refuelling, have the task of long-range interdiction of Soviet air and naval bases in support of operations on NATO's northern flank. Other systems are also currently under development to enhance Tornado's survival chances in a heavily-defended hostile environment over the next decade; one of them, developed by Ferranti and aptly named Penetrate, was undergoing flight trials at the Royal Aerospace Establishment, Farnborough, in 1989.

Below: A Harrier GR3 of 233 Operational Conversion Unit (OCU), the world's premier V/STOL unit. The aircraft is on final approach for a conventional landing. *(Robbie Shaw)*

Designed for both Tornado and the European Fighter Aircraft, Penetrate will enhance an aircraft's ability to perform covert high-speed low-level penetration at night and in adverse weather, using a radio altimeter for accurate terrain-referenced navigation. The output is displayed in the form of a digital map and is also coupled to the pilot's head-up display. The pilot can select progressive HUD enhancements, depending on the visibility. These range from obstruction cues, through ridgeline overlays, to full perspective displays of the terrain. Other contenders in this field for the Tornado's mid-life update are the British Aerospace Terprom and GEC Avionics Spartan systems.

Above: On the ground the two-seat Harrier T4 looks rather ungainly. The majority of T4s are on the strength of 233 OCU, and one of its aircraft is seen taxying back to disperal at its Wittering base. *(Robbie Shaw)*

The concept of the long-range hi-lo-hi sortie, which would be the pattern used by No. 1 Group's Tornado squadrons in time of war, was first proved on 8 November 1982, when a Tornado GR.1 of No. 9 Squadron (which subsequently moved to Germany as part of 2 ATAF) flew from Honington to carry out a simulated airfield attack on RAF Akrotiri in Cyprus and then returned to base after covering a distance of 4,300 nautical miles. The Tornado was accompanied by a Buccaneer S.Mk. 2, also from Honington and fitted with a 'buddy-buddy' refuelling pod.

Soon after take-off, the two aircraft made rendezvous with a Victor K.2 tanker off the coast of East Anglia to make sure that their refuelling systems were fully serviceable, then set course at between 18,000 and 24,000 feet over France and Sardinia to Sicily, where they again refuelled from a Victor tanker. Rendezvous with the latter was achieved by using the Tornado's radar in the air-to-air mode. The two aircraft then set course for Cyprus, descending to 2,000 feet 300 miles west of the island for the low-level refuelling operation. When this was completed the Tornado went down to 200 feet and increased speed to 480 knots, running-in from 100 miles out to sea. The radar was switched on in the final minutes of the approach, and the crew found that the offset error was so small that the equipment was not really necessary in carrying out a visual attack — although it would have been necessary in carrying out an accurate blind attack at night. After

After-landing checks being carried out by the pilot of a 233 OCU Harrier GR5. *(Robbie Shaw)*

successfully completing its attack the Tornado again made rendez-vous with a Victor tanker off Sicily at high level, then re-crossed Sardinia and France at 20-27,000 feet *en route* for Honington. The aircraft landed after a total flight time of twelve hours ten minutes.

Today, in addition to their normal training routines, the crews of Nos. 27 and 617 Squadrons gain valuable operational experience in long-range attack techniques through participation in NATO exercises — of which more later — and participation in the annual USAF Strategic Air Command Bombing and Navigation Competition. In this, the most demanding of its kind in the world, the Tornado crews have achieved spectacular results and have shown themselves to be well fitted for their operational task; but their success hinges on one vital factor, without which the RAF's effectiveness as a striking force in any theatre other than central Europe would be severely curtailed.

A trio of Harrier GR5s from 233 OCU in echelon starboard. Note the refuelling probes on the port side of the cockpit canopy.
*(Robbie Shaw)*

## The Tanker Force

The Falklands War of 1982, with its attendant need for long-range deployments, revealed the full potential of air-to-air refuelling (AAR) and also the shortcomings of the RAF's tanker force at that time. At the outbreak of hostilities the RAF's tanker force consisted of twenty-three Victor K.2s belonging to Nos. 55 and 57 Squadrons, together with the Victor OCU, all based at RAF Marham; it was planned to supplement and eventually replace these aircraft with VC-10s converted to the tanker role, but the first of these conversions did not fly until June 1982.

The Falklands operations seriously overstretched the Victor tanker squadrons, and during their deployment to Ascension Island during the period of hostilities many of their routine AAR tasks in support of NATO had to be undertaken by USAF KC-135A aircraft of the European Tanker Task Force, based at Fairford and Mildenhall. Such was the urgency surrounding the requirement for additional tankers that on 30 April 1982, with active operations in the Falklands about to begin, the possibility of convering six Vulcan B.2s to the tanker role was discussed by representatives of the RAF, MoD and British Aerospace at the latter's Woodford aerodrome; approval for this step was given on 4 May, and the first Vulcan tanker conversion was delivered to No. 50 Squadron at RAF Waddington on 23 June. The six converted Vulcans remained on service until May 1984, when No. 50 Squadron disbanded after the first VC-10 tankers came on stream. To provide an additional AAR capability, Marshalls of Cambridge received an urgent request, soon after the Argentine invasion of the Falklands, to install flight refuelling probes in the RAF's Hercules transports. Design work began on 15 April and the first aircraft was test-flown ten days later, being deployed to Ascension on 14 May. Subsequent aircraft were also modified in record time, with fourteen Hercules receivers being delivered in as many days.

The Air Staff immediately followed up with a request for the installation of a Flight Refuelling hose drum unit to provide a centreline tanker capability. Four aircraft were converted to the tanker configuration, all four being completed within twelve weeks. Together with the RAF Victors the Hercules tankers went into continuous service on the South Atlantic route.

The GR5 version of the Harrier has no shortage of pylons to carry its hardware, though on this occasion only the inboards are occupied — with fuel tanks. This aircraft belongs to No 1 Squadron, the first operational squadron to equip with the GR5.
*(Robbie Shaw)*

Above: A four-ship formation of 226 OCU Jaguars about to take off on a routine training sortie. This formation comprises two of each variant, the GR1A and T2A. *(Robbie Shaw)*

Opposite: The 'wraparound' camouflage is evident on this Jaguar GR1A of 226 OCU. *(Robbie Shaw)*

Meanwhile, work on bringing the VC-10 tankers into service proceeded. The original batch of nine secondhand aircraft had been purchased by the MoD in 1979. Five were Standard VC-10s operated first by BOAC and later by Gulf Air; the other four were ex-East African Airways aircraft and were stretched Super VC-10s. Basically, conversion work, after extensive refurbishing, involved the installation of two underwing Flight Refuelling Mk. 32/2800 pods and an FR Mk. 17 internal hose reel in the rear fuselage.

Installation of the Mk. 17 hose drum involved cutting a hole in the pressurised structure and removing the rear underfloor freight hold to make room. New pressure bulkheads were provided fore and aft of the cutout, with new sidewalls and a pressure floor over the top. To carry the wing pods, new structure was added between the spars, to which the pylons are permanently attached. Each pylon carries floodlights to illuminate the aircraft for night refuelling, and a floodlight under the rear fuselage picks out the engine nacelles. Fuel capacity (which is classified) was increased by bolting five cylindrical fuel tanks to the cabin floor. To install the fuselage fuel tanks a hole had to be cut in the upper fuselage of the Standard VC-10s; those on the Super VC-10s were installed through the forward cargo door, which was then sealed. Baggage racks were removed from the tank bay and most of the windows were blanked off.

The first conversion, designated VC-10 K.2A (ZA140) was delivered to the RAF VC-10 OCU at RAF Brize Norton on 25 July 1983, and No. 101 Squadron re-formed on the type at the same location on 1 May 1984, its aircrews drawn from VC-10 transport and Victor and Vulcan AAR squadrons. The crew of a VC-10 tanker comprises two pilots, a navigator and a flight engineer, who is also responsible for hose-drogue deployment and fuel transfer; all three refuelling points and their receiver aircraft are monitored by a ventrally-mounted TV camera with a display at the flight engineer's station. Transfer rate from the wing pods is up to 350 gal/min through a fifty foot hose, and from the centreline station 500 gal/min through an eighty-one foot hose/drogue. The drogue itself also carries twelve aiming lights for night refuelling.

In RAF service, the VC-10 tanker is designated K.2 (standard version) and K.3 (super version). Space is retained forward of the cabin tanks for seventeen passenger seats in the K.2 and eighteen seats in the K.3 to carry support personnel on extended deployments. A galley and toilet is located immediately aft of the cockpit. The port-front door has been modified to include a parachute-escape chute, so crew entry is now via the starboard door.

The RAF bought a second batch of fourteen ex-British Airways VC-10s in 1981; of these, ten were suitable for tanker conversion and the other four for spares. The aircraft were placed in storage at RAF Abingdon, and in February 1990 British Aerospace and the Flight Refuelling Group were awarded contracts to convert five of them to K.3 standard. Under the same contract, British Aerospace and FR are also to convert eight of No. 10 Squadron's VC-10 transports into two-point tankers. They will eventually provide replacements for the remaining Victor K.2 tankers when the latter reach the end of their fatigue lives.

By the time they reach the RAF squadrons, the VC-10 tankers are virtually new aircraft; first of all they are stripped down for an in-depth survey, then the engines and landing gear are removed and returned to the manufacturers for refurbishing. The aircraft is gutted of systems; some are refurbished, others replaced with new items. All movable surfaces are removed and the airframe is subjected to a detailed scrutiny for corrosion, fatigue and damage. The thoroughness of the inspection is such that, on the first VC-10 to be converted, British Aerospace uncovered some 60,000 items in need of replacement or repair.

The Falklands War revealed another AAR requirement — for a long-range, wide-body tanker. The RAF evaluated several wide-body types in 1982, but in the end the choice was narrowed down to the McDonnell Douglas DC-10 and the Lockheed TriStar 500, both of which were available on the second-hand market. The RAF would have preferred the DC-10, because the KC-10 conversion had already proved the concept of the aircraft's use as a tanker and because it would have given the RAF a degree of equipment commonality with the USAF. However, the available budget finally dictated the choice of the TriStar, six of which were purchased from British Airways and converted to the tanker role by Marshalls of Cambridge. Conversion involved the fitting of nine extra tanks in the underfloor baggage hold, carrying 100,000 lb of fuel, and a twinpack of Mk. 17T HDUs on the

Below: The Jaguar force has gradually been run down over the past few years. From a peak of eight squadrons in the nineteen seventies there are now just three, one of which, No. 41, operates in the tactical reconnaissance role. *(Robbie Shaw)*

Opposite: Odiham is the home of the RAF's support helicopter, and from this location No. 240 OCU trains crews for both the Puma and Chinook. *(Robbie Shaw)*

rear fuselage centreline. The wings were also plumbed for Mk. 32 pods, which can be fitted as required. The underfloor fuel tank arrangement left the passenger cabin free to carry up to 120 troops, their equipment, and freight.

The first TriStars entered service with No. 216 Squadron at RAF Brize Norton on 1 November 1984. Three more aircraft were later purchased from Pan American, and these also went into service with No. 216 Squadron after conversion. With No. 216 Squadron declared operational in the dual tanker/transport role, one of the two units of the Marham Victor Tanker Wing — No. 57 Squadron — disbanded, leaving No. 55 Squadron as the only Victor K.2 unit. This squadron was still operating from Marham at the beginning of 1990, with fourteen aircraft selected from the original pool of twenty-three.

Below: Although not as robust as the Wessex, the Puma is a popular helicopter with the operators, in this case 33 Squadron based at Odiham. *(Robbie Shaw)*

No. 1 Group's AAR organisation has another asset which is often overlooked: the Buccaneers of the Lossiemouth Strike Wing. These aircraft can be fitted with a refuelling pod and, although they come under the control of No. 18 Group and would generally support each other on long-range anti-shipping missions, they could also refuel Tornados flying deep-penetration missions in the north.

The role of No. 1 Group's AAR resources is threefold: the support of air defence forces, support for offensive forces, and support of the maritime and transport fleets. In time of war the RAF's air defence aircraft would be spread very thinly, and the AWACS E-3 fleet would also be overstretched. The use of AAR is a cost-effective means of sortie extension, allowing more flexibility and mobility. In the offensive field, aircraft near the front

Above: The largest operational squadron in the RAF is No. 72, which flies the Wessex HC.2 from Aldergrove in support of the Army. *(Robbie Shaw)*

line, such as Jaguars and Harriers, would not use AAR, but they would need it if carrying out long-range missions against targets in northern Norway, or for rapid deployment to that area. The main user, as we have seen, would be the Tornado GR.1. AAR is also the natural force multiplier of No. 18 Group's Nimrod maritime patrol aircraft. In general, the RAF's tanker force is adequate for the tasks it has to perform — or will be, when the older aircraft are phased out and replaced by newer ones. The dual tanker/transport concept is excellent with enormous attendant flexibility; the TriStars can airlift a thousand troops to any trouble spot thousands of miles from home base, and at the same time refuel supporting fighter-bombers.

The main problem that has to be overcome in future RAF AAR developments is one of vulnerability. It is necessary to improve aircraft survivability by providing them with protection such as hardened aircraft shelters, effective camouflage, jamming pods and

chaff. Tankers are especially vulnerable when refuelling other aircraft, so developments are needed to enable them to carry out the process in the shortest possible time.

## Tactical Support
No. 1 Group also controls the RAF's home-based Tactical Support Force, which was previously administered by a separate formation, No. 38 Group. The teeth of this force is the V/STOL British Aerospace Harrier GR.5, which at the end of 1989 partially equipped No. 233 Operational Conversion Unit at RAF Wittering and No. 1 Squadron at the same base. The introduction of the GR.5, intended to replace the earlier Harrier GR.3, fell behind schedule in 1987/88 because of the need to modify certain items of equipment and to replace the Ferranti FIN 1076 Inertial Navigation System (INS), which failed to meet requirements.

The UK based Chinook HC.1 squadron is No. 7. From its Odiham base the unit's aircraft are kept busy all over the country, from the Scottish Highlands to the Isle of Wight, where this shot of an aircraft wearing special markings for the squadron anniversary was taken. *(Robbie Shaw)*

The main modification involved the GR.5's ejection seat, which accidentally fired from a trials aircraft in 1987, killing a British Aerospace test pilot. The modifications include guarding the seat's manual overhead operating rod, and modifying a valve in the emergency oxygen system contained in the seat. While these modifications were being carried out, Harrier GR.5s in RAF service were restricted to operating below 10,000 feet, precluding such activities as air-to-air refuelling and weather avoidance.

Operational trials with the Ferranti FIN 1075 showed that the equipment was unreliable, with a history of malfunctions. According to Ferranti, this was because problems had arisen with the aircraft cooling system, allowing water ingress to the INS. In late 1988 investigations were under way to remedy the situation, but MoD (RAF), anxious to speed up the GR.5's full operational capability, decided to order thirty-two ANS-130 INS sets from Litton Industries of California as a stopgap replacement, deliveries to be completed by August 1989, at a cost of up to £3.5 million.

The Harrier GR.5 is a very important aircraft on the RAF's inventory. Built jointly by British Aerospace and McDonnell Douglas, it differs considerably from previous Harriers in that it has a new super-critical aerofoil wing with a greater area and span, providing an extra 2,000 lb fuel uplift. The main wing torque box structure is manufactured of carbon fibre composite (CFC), with metal leading edges. It also has large CFC slotted flaps and ailerons whose movement is linked with nozzle deflection at short take-off (STO) unstick, to provide greater wing lift capacity, enabling operation at a much higher all-up weight.

Longitudinal strakes and a lateral fence — lift improvement devices (LIDS) — have been incorporated on the underfuselage gun pod system to capture ground-reflected jets in VTOL to give a better ground cushion and reduce hot gas circulation. The GR.5 also has Leading Edge Root Extensions (LERX) to enhance its air combat agility by improving turn rate, and a raised cockpit with a bubble canopy to improve the pilot's view.

Above: Primary task of the Chinook force is to support the Army and as such, 7 Squadron frequently operates in the Salisbury Plain training area. It was at that location where this shot of troops emplaning was taken. *(Robbie Shaw)*

The UK Ministry of Defence originally ordered sixty-two Harrier GR.5s, and planned to update part of the existing GR.3 fleet for service through the 1990s. The latter scheme was subsequently dropped, and thirty-four more GR.5s ordered instead early in 1988.

The Harrier GR.5 has a payload of 16,700 lb. Maximum internal fuel is 7,500 lb, leaving a further 9,200 lb ordnance payload. It is

powered by a Rolls-Royce Pegasus 11-61 vectored thrust, low bypass turbofan developing a maximum thrust of 23,500 lb without reheat. It is an economical engine; in one minute from brake release, accelerating to a speed of 400 knots, the GR.5 burns only 220 lb of fuel. In addition to its external stores, the aircraft is armed with two Royal Ordnance Aden 25 mm cannon, carried in under-belly pods.

Workhorse of the transport fleet is the Lockheed Hercules. This photograph was taken in 1985 when the aircraft still wore 'Mercy Flight' titling having taken part in relief flights in Africa. *(Robbie Shaw)*

Below: The VC-10 C1 has given the RAF splendid service and, in its first decade with No. 10 Squadron, operated the RAF's airline type schedule services to the Middle and Far East. The type is still used extensively on short and medium haul tasks; the TriStar now undertaking most of the long haul work. *(Robbie Shaw)*

Already, updates are under development which will make the Harrier GR.5 an effective weapons system into the 21st Century. It is to be equipped with a unique Missile Approach Warning System (MAW), developed by Plessey Avionics Ltd under a £10 million UK MoD contract. This will provide an active warning system intended to warn Harrier pilots of enemy surface-to-air or air-to-air missiles approaching from the rear. Once a missile has been detected, MAW will automatically trigger electronic self-defence systems such as infra-red flares or chaff.

MAW has been designed primarily as a counter to infra-red homing missiles such as the Soviet SA-7 Grail and modern air-to-air weapons similar in principle to the AIM-9 Sidewinder. These weapons cannot be detected by Radar Warning Receivers (RWR) which work by detecting radar pulses emitted by fire control radars or the seeker heads of active radar-guided missiles. Heat-seeking missiles such as the inexpensive hand-held SA-7 are entirely passive and extremely hard to detect; also, they are so numerous that they represent a major and growing threat to combat aircraft operating at even ultra-low altitude over the battlefield.

The new system, which weighs only 25 lb (12 kg), is basically a pulse doppler radar which will be mounted in the GR.5's tail boom. MAW is designed to be used at low altitude and high speed and to minimise false alarms. The net result is that the survivability of the Harrier GR.5 will be enhanced enormously. Along with MAW the aircraft will carry an RWR, an internal radar jammer and chaff and flare dispensers.

Opposite: Most of the Hercules fleet have now been fitted with in-flight refuelling probes, as seen on this Hercules C1P on the ramp at Benson during a deployment from its Lyneham base. *(Robbie Shaw)*

Another item in the update programme is a moving map display, developed by GEC Avionics under a £7 million MoD (Procurement Executive) contract. The company is to produce 100 Digital Colour Map Units (DCMU). This system, a private venture which has been under development for some years, is unique in its ability to store map data for an area the size of Europe in one avionics box with no moving parts. GEC Avionics also provides the Forward Looking Infra Red (FLIR) system for the Harrier GR.5; this system, which has also been selected for the Tornado GR.1, was the subject of a £48 million order from the MoD in 1985. It consists of an FLIR

sensor and processing equipment which produce an image of the scene ahead of the aircraft. The image is displayed on the pilot's HUD along with the normal HUD symbology. The FLIR itself is based on the UK Thermal Imaging Common Module Class III (TICM II) and breaks new ground by being the first FLIR to be used by the RAF as a pilot's night flying aid rather than just a reconnaissance system. The update is to include a new Smiths Industries Head Up/Head Down display and cockpit displays compatible with Night Vision Goggles (NVG). The modified aircraft, designated Harrier GR.7, will be capable of flying low altitude round-the-clock missions in all but very bad weather. Some aircraft are being completed from the outset as GR.7s, and the whole of the RAF's Harrier GR.5 force will be brought up to GR.7 standard during the 1990s.

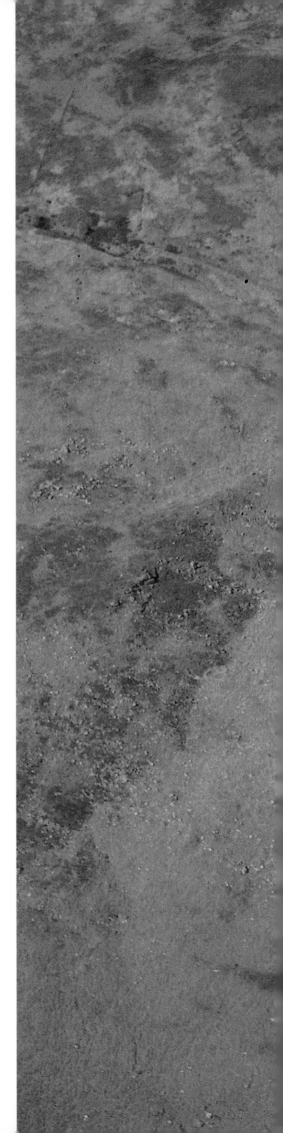

A further, logical development is the addition of a multi-mode radar; this is currently under advanced study by both McDonnell Douglas and British Aerospace. The idea is to fit the aircraft with both night-attack avionics and a pulse-doppler multi-mode radar capable of handling beyond visual range (BVR) air-to-air missiles and anti-ship missiles such as Sea Eagle or Harpoon. It will also be capable of carrying out ground-mapping, terrain avoidance and ground attack functions. The aim is to give the Harrier far greater flexibility in weapons delivery, amounting, in simple terms, to the ability to fly low and fast in dirty weather and still hit a small moving point target. Add to the radar the night attack capabilities of the FLIR and Night Vision Goggles, and one has a truly formidable aircraft.

In time of war No. 233 OCU's Harriers would reinforce the Harrier squadrons on the Central Front, while No. 1 Squadron's aircraft would deploy to Norway in defence of the northern flank, attacking enemy troops and invasion ships with BL755 cluster bombs and laser-guided weapons. In one recent deployment — Exercise Snow Falcon 88, which took place in February 1988 — four Harrier GR.3s and a T.4 two-seater operated in temperatures of minus twenty-five degrees centigrade from the Royal Norwegian Air Force base at Bardufoss, 150 miles north of the Arctic Circle. During the week-long deployment the aircraft flew seventy-five sorties and achieved an availability rate of nine-five per cent, a tribute as much to the ground crews — who spent up to five hours a day in the open turning the aircraft round — as to the Harrier's ruggedness.

The mountains and valleys of Wales, and the uncluttered airspace off its coast make Brawdy an ideal location for a Tactical Weapons Unit. No. 1 TWU comprises 79 and 234 Squadrons. an aircraft from the latter unit is depicted here. *(Robbie Shaw)*

Below: The successful BAe 146 airliner is used by The Queen's Flight at Benson. Two BAe 146 CC2s are on strength, whilst delivery of a third is imminent. *(Robbie Shaw)*

The second element of the Tactical Support Force is the Jaguar force, comprising Nos. 6 and 54 Squadrons in the strike role and No. 41 Squadron in the tactical reconnaissance role at RAF Coltishall, in Norfolk, together with the Jaguar OCU (No. 226) at RAF Lossiemouth. The Jaguar GR.1 is a single-seat strike aircraft whose principal role is the direct tactical support of ground forces;

powered by two Rolls-Royce Adour Mk. 104 turbojets, it carries a wide variety of offensive weaponry and has a built-in armament of two 30 mm Aden guns. At low level it is very hard to detect with the naked eye and produces a very small radar signature; its handling character-istics are good and it has a low gust response, although at transonic speed and with certain weapons combinations — four 1,000 lb bombs on the inboard pylons, an ECM pod or an AIM-9L Sidewinder on one side, a Matra Phimat chaff dispenser on the other and a centreline fuel tank, for example — it is sensitive in pitch.

The aircraft is fitted with two weapon guidance systems: a Laser Ranging and Marked Target Seeker (LRMTS) and a Navigation and Weapon Aiming Subsystem (NAV-WASS), both developed by Ferranti. NAVWASS is controlled by a Ferranti FIN 1064 Inertial Navigation System, with a control and display unit mounted on the cockpit coam-ing. Jaguar pilots have a very high degree of confidence in the 1064, which is pre-programmed before a sortie with all the relevant data involving waypoints, initial point, target, groundspeed, bank angle at weapons release and so on. The system continuously computes the impact point, the information being

Above: The Andover E3 aircraft of 115 Squadron have adopted a high visibility red and white paint scheme, and are equipped with high intensity strobe lights. This helps them to be seen by other aircraft whilst calibrating navigation aids at busy airfields. *(Robbie Shaw)*

Opposite: No. 32 Squadron's fleet of BAe 125 aircraft is kept busy on VIP tasks throughout the UK and Europe. This CC1 variant was photographed on take-off from Leuchars. *(Robbie Shaw)*

passed to the pilot via his HUD. The Continuously Computed Impact Point (CCIP) takes velocity, slant range, altitude and ballistic inputs and calculates the impact point for guns, bombs or rockets. The impact point is displayed on the HUD, and when the sight mark crosses the target the pilot manually releases his weapons. The other available mode is the Continuously Computed Release Point (CCRP), in which the sight mark on the HUD is depressed by a few degrees. The pilot initiates weapons release when the mark hits the target, and the ranging sensor, slaved to the

sight reticle, takes an instantaneous slant range measurement. The pilot starts to pull up and the computer begins calculating target range based on the initial velocity, range and ballistic inputs, as well as range to bomb impact point. The weapons are released automatically when the two ranges coincide. Of the two modes, CCIP is the more flexible and is used in close support, when targets are numerous; CCRP is used against a pre-selected target based on co-ordinates entered before take-off or during flight, and is accurate enough to permit a blind attack.

The Jaguar is fitted with a Marconi Space and Defence Systems ARI 18223 radar warning receiver, which presents information to the pilot by lamps on a display panel. Forward-and rearward-facing antennae are mounted on the aircraft's vertical fin. The primary defences against an air threat are an ECM pod, chaff and flares, but Jaguar can also carry the Sidewinder AAM.

Like the UK-based Harrier force, No. 1 Group's Jaguar squadrons can be deployed in support of NATO's central and northern fronts. In the latter case, Jaguars would typically be deployed to the offshore R Nor AF base in Andoya to carry out reconnaissance and strike sorties against enemy invasion forces. The Jaguar is scheduled to remain in first-line service until the mid-1990s, when it will be replaced by the European Fighter Aircraft (see chapter two).

The third element of the Tactical Support Force is the helicopter force, comprising the Odiham Wing — No. 7 Squadron with Chinooks and No. 33 Squadron with Pumas, together with No. 240 OCU equipped with both types — and No. 72 Squadron, based at RAF Aldergrove in Northern Ireland and operating the Wessex HC.2. In 1983 the UK Ministry of Defence issued Air Staff Requirement 404 for a new medium-lift helicopter to replace both the Puma and Wessex; the requirement was for between seventy-five and 125 aircraft, each with a gross weight of 18,000 lb and capable of carrying thirty fully-equipped troops. The aircraft must be twin-engined, with a cruising speed of between 140 and 150 knots and 65 nm combat radius. The helicopter, stated AST 404, must also have a day/night, poor-weather capability.

Below: The rotary element of The Queen's Flight comprises two Wessex HCC4 which have been in service for twenty-one years. (Robbie Shaw)

Above: In addition to the training role, the Gazelle is used for VIP work by 32 Squadron at Northolt who have four Gazelle HT3s on strength. (Robbie Shaw)

In April 1987, Defence Secretary George Younger announced the Government's intention to order twenty-five Agusta/Westland EH.101 utility helicopters as a first step towards meeting the Army's future battlefield support requirement. In 1988, however, with the EH.101 flight development programme well under way, senior British Army officers were expressing concern about the EH.101's survivability, crash tolerance and payload capability as defined by Military Specification 1290. One opinion school sees a combination of the Boeing Chinook and the Sikorsky UH-60 Black Hawk as a better alternative; however, the Black Hawk can only carry fifteen troops, and while the Chinook could be used to ferry additional men and equipment, it could not operate directly over the forward edge of the battle area, where it would be intensely vulnerable. In several cases, the EH.101 can combine the role of Chinook and Black Hawk in one airframe, making the purchase of fewer units necessary. But the vulnerability problem remains, and operating 'soft' helicopters close to the enemy lines is a recipe for disaster.

Wyton is home to the Canberra T17 aircraft of 360 Squadron, and some of the aircraft have recently been updated to T17A standard. This aircraft was photographed off the south coast whilst operating with Royal Navy ships in the Portland area. *(Robbie Shaw)*

Below: Just visible is the wire
towing the banner target behind
this 100 Squadron Canberra PR7.
*(Gordon Scott)*

## The Transport Force

Also tasked with the direct support of the Army in the field are two Lockheed Hercules units, Nos. 47 and 70 Squadrons, which form part of the Hercules Wing at RAF Lyneham, in Wiltshire. The Wing's other two squadrons, Nos. 24 and 30, are assigned mainly to route flying. Also at Lyneham is the Hercules OCU,, No. 242. Sixty Hercules are in service, including six C.1K tankers and sixteen C.1P receivers, all of which are operated by Nos. 47 and 70 Squadrons. The operational tasks of these two squadrons are co-ordinated by the Transport Support Operations Room of the Support Training Squadron of No. 242 OCU, whose staff arrange for the aircrew, aircraft and paratroops or air-drop loads to come together at the appointed time. All air-drop loads dropped by the Hercules Force are prepared, loaded into, and despatched from the aircraft by personnel of No. 47 Air Despatch Squadron, Royal Corps of Transport, which is also based at RAF Lyneham. The Hercules Force may be called upon to mount up to thirty aircraft in the TS role at any one time for the tactical deployment of paratroops and supplies direct from Lyneham to anywhere within NATO Europe.

Below: Just visible is the wire towing the banner target behind this 100 Squadron Canberra PR7. *(Gordon Scott)*

Thirty aircraft of the Lyneham Wing are 'stretched' Hercules C.3s, their fuselages lengthened by Marshalls of Cambridge to increase the internal volume of the cargo hold from 127.4 m$^3$ to 171.5 m$^3$, allowing — for example — seven pallet loads to be carried instead of the Hercules C.1's five. These aircraft are mostly used by Nos. 24 and 30 Squadrons on their worldwide operations.

Also forming part of the long-range transport forces is No. 10 Squadron, which operates thirteen VC-10 C.1 aircraft on scheduled services around the world from RAF Brize Norton, in Oxfordshire. The RAF's VC-10 transports are hybrid aircraft, having the airframe of the standard civil VC-10 combined with Rolls-Royce Conway 301 engines and the increased fuel capacity of the Super VC-10.

The Hercules and the VC-10 will remain the primary RAF transport aircraft until 1999 under present planning. After that they will be replaced by a new design, the Future International Military Airlifter, which is now under study by British Aerospace, Lockheed-

Above: The eldest of the four marks of Canberra used by No. 100 Squadron at Wyton is the B2, illustrated here at its Wyton base. *(Robbie Shaw)*

Georgia of the USA, Aérospatiale of France, and MBB of West Germany. The FIMA will also replace the Lockheed C-130 Hercules in USAF service, and the C.160 Transall in the Luftwaffe and French Air Force.

Current plans call for two FIMA production lines, one in Europe and one in the United States. Including projected tanker and maritime patrol variants, production is estimated at between 700 and 1,000 aircraft. Preliminary development was scheduled to start in 1989, with engineering development starting in 1993. This would be followed by a first flight in 1997, followed by service deliveries two years later.

The RAF's sole high level reconnaissance asset now is the Canberra PR9s of No. 1 Photographic Reconnaissance Unit at Wyton. The aircraft are frequently called upon to undertake survey work worldwide and have recently adopted the hemp colour scheme. *(Robbie Shaw)*

The basic design criteria in the FIMA study were improved payload, range and cruise speed over the present generation of medium-lift transports; a wide optimised cargo hold including a load bearing tail ramp; very good field performance obtained at medium cost; a three-man crew comprising two pilots and a loadmaster, which means that the systems in both the hold and cockpit will need to be highly automated; improved passenger comfort levels; and a high degree of tolerance to battle damage. The choice of engine — advanced turboprop or turbofan — was still open in 1990, although the participating nations had agreed that the aircraft should have four (the French and Germans had originally wanted two). The aircraft will be fitted with heavy duty C-130-type landing gear; this and its advanced avionics will permit operation from semi-prepared grass fields or desert strips by day and night in all weathers. The aircraft's wing will be optimised for long-range cruise and have high lift devices for STOL performance.

As far as the RAF is concerned, the main doubt is whether the present transport force will remain viable for another decade. Refurbishing programmes will probably keep the Hercules fleet reasonably intact, but the VC-10s may have to be replaced by an off-the-shelf airliner purchase in order to bridge the gap.

Below: The black and yellow target towing stripes readily identify this 100 Squadron Canberra as the TT18 variant. These were converted from the B2. *(Robbie Shaw)*

Above: The goose insignia on the tail and lack of Magnetic Anomoly Detector (MAD) aerial identify this Nimrod as an R1 of 51 Squadron. *(Robbie Shaw)*

### The Tactical Weapons Units

No. 1 Group RAF Strike Command exercises operational control over the RAF's two Tactical Weapons Units, No. 1 TWU at RAF Brawdy and No. 2 TWU at RAF Chivenor. Both are equipped with the British Aerospace Hawk T.1A. Each TWU has two squadrons with 'shadow' identities: Nos. 63 and 151 Squadrons at Chivenor, and Nos. 79 and 234 Squadrons at Brawdy. The Hawk is a first-class fighting trainer, and will remain so for several years to come; the design is constantly being developed and the TWU Hawks have a war role that can include ground attack or air defence (see chapter two).

Student pilots, fresh from No. 4 Flying Training School at RAF Valley, Anglesey, spend about four months at one of the TWUs, where they are taught the tactical principles of fast jet operation in the air defence and offensive support roles. The course is progressively demanding, being designed to filter out all those who are not able to attain — and more importantly maintain — the capacity to cope with the very high workload required in today's first-line tactical squadrons. Successful graduates then pass on to the appropriate OCU.

During the hot and dry summer months in Hong Kong the 28 Squadron Wessex HC2s are frequently called upon to assist the local authorities in putting out fires on remote and inaccessible hillsides.
*(Robbie Shaw)*

## Other Units

Other units under the control of No. 1 Group are as follows.

No.115 Squadron is based at RAF Benson and operates British Aerospace Andover C.1 and E.3 aircraft on radar and navaid calibration duties, supporting RAF facilities around the world. The Andover replaced the Varsity T.1 and the Argosy E.1 in this role, and will remain in service for some years to come.

No. 32 Squadron, at RAF Northolt, is the RAF's sole communications squadron, operating twelve British Aerospace HS125 twin-jet executive aircraft under the designation HS125 CC.1, CC.2 and CC.3, some Andover CC.2s and three Gazelle HCC4 helicopters fitted out as VIP transports.

At RAF Benson, the Queen's Flight operates two British Aerospace 146 C.2s and two Wessex HCC4 helicopters. The British Aerospace 146 replaced the Andover CC.2 in service with the Queen's Flight.

Concentrated at RAF Wyton, near Huntingdon, are Strike Command's remaining Canberras. Five Canberra PR.9s are still operational with No.1 Photographic Reconnaissance Unit, while No. 100 Squadron operates Canberras of various marks in the target facilities role, providing 'silent' targets to train, test and probe the UK air defences. No. 360 Squadron, with Canberra T.17s, is an ECM training unit, its task to simulate the Warsaw Pact ECM threat and to exercise the UK air defences in overcoming it. A small number of Canberra B.2s and T.4s continue to serve with No. 231 OCU.

The other Wyton-based unit is No. 51 Squadron, which operates three British Aerospace Nimrod R.1 aircraft on electronic intelligence work.

Overseas units under the control of No. 1 Group are No. 28 Squadron (Wessex) in Hong Kong, operating in support of security forces, and No. 84 Squadron (Wessex) in Cyprus, operating in support of the UN peace-keeping force and also on SAR duties for UK-based aircraft using the Armament Practice Camp at Akrotiri.

The Wessex HC2 of 28 Squadron at Sek Kong are used primarily in support of the Ghurka Regiments. The helicopter is a necessity in Hong Kong to reach the many parts of the territory accessible only by helicopter. This Wessex is departing a landing site in the Castle Peak Range having deplaned its load of troops. *(Robbie Shaw)*

# CHAPTER TWO
## No. 11 Group, Strike Command

The task of providing the air defence of the United Kingdom falls to No. 11 Group RAF Strike Command. In summary, its operational commitments are to give warning of any aircraft or missile threat to the United Kingdom; to provide an air defence force and its associated control system wherever the need arises, including air defence for ships of the Royal Navy; and to exercise control of the United Kingdom airspace in peace and war.

The air defence element of the Command forms part of a unified system under the Supreme Allied Commander Europe, with the UK forming one of four air defence regions. It is a NATO requirement that commanders with responsibilities other than air defence shall appoint a deputy for air defence only, and so, whilst the AOC-in-C Strike Command is the Air Defence Commander and Commander of the NATO UK Air Defence Region, he delegates his responsibilities for the direct day-to-day operational control to the AOC No. 11 Group.

The responsibility is enormous, for the UK Air Defence Region covers an area of four million square miles. Northwards, it extends as far as the southern tip of Iceland, and to the south it covers northern France and the Netherlands. Its north-eastern flank reaches out to the coast of Norway. If it were overlaid across continental Europe, it would cover an area bounded by the Pyrenees, Denmark, Czechoslovakia and Poland.

Operational control of the UK Air Defence Region is exercised from the Strike Command Air Defence Operations Centre (ADOC) at High Wycombe, with overall control from the Air Force Operations Room (AFOR) in the Ministry of Defence, Whitehall. Basically, the system of centralised command and control is not very different from that which contributed so much to winning the Battle of Britain half a century ago, with its sectors, regional operations centres, subordinate control and reporting posts, and the Chain Home network of RDF stations.

Today, the ADOC has a completely centralised command picture of the UK Air Defence Region. The Sector Operations Centres (SOCs) exercise tactical control over their respective regions and over the Command and Reporting Centres (CRCs) which are responsible for the tracking of hostiles and the control of interceptors. Limited backup tracking and fighter control are provided by Command and Reporting Posts (CRPs), while the radar sites form the front line.

## The Threat

The principal threat to the UK environment comes from low-flying, all-weather aircraft armed with long-range missiles and protected by advanced electronic countermeasures. The Soviet Air and Naval Air Forces now have a considerable flight refuelling capability (a technique which the USSR was slow to develop) and the threat could materialise from any direction, with radar sites and air defence airfields priority one targets for Tu-26 Backfire and Su-24 Fencer aircraft armed with weapons like the AS-9 Kyle, a missile fitted with a passive radar seeker and having a range of about fity miles.

## Radar Defences

By the mid-1970s, it was realised that the existing UK air defence radar system, known as UKADGE (United Kingdom Air Defence Ground Environment), with its fixed radars — some of which were located close to the nerve centres of the air defence network — was becoming increasingly vulnerable to the new generation of Soviet strike aircraft and their associated anti-radiation weaponry. If effective air defence cover was to be provided into the 21st Century, what was needed was a revised system combining a centralised command structure with a decentralised sensor network that was secure, survivable and capable of functioning even after sustaining substantial damage. The new system would be based on advanced portable ground radars, enabling sensors to be deployed almost anywhere in the UK, and new telecommunications technology providing a nationwide network of lines and exchanges which would continue to route both voice and data transmissions along any path so long as some sort of physical connection remained.

Project definition of the new concept was carried out by the Plessey Company on behalf of the Ministry of Defence, and by the middle of 1979 the idea was shown to be feasible, with at least one practical design approach. As a result, Air Staff Requirement 888 was drawn up, calling for an Improved UK Air Defence Ground Environment (IUKADGE) to replace the existing Linesman/Mediator system which had been introduced as the last major update in the early 1970s. The latter system went some way towards improving the dissemination of radar information, and was updated to provide an automated means of distributing a recognised tactical air picture among SOCs in UKADGE, NADGE and Strida (the last two being comparable systems in Continental NATO

Below: With the introduction of the E-3 Sentry AEW1, the hard working Shackleton AEW2s of No. 8 Squadron will be gracefully retired. Who could have envisaged that these aircraft would still be in service forty years after they were first delivered to the RAF.
*(Robbie Shaw)*

Opposite: It is a credit to the groundcrews and technicians of No. 8 Squadron that they have been able to keep the engines and other systems of the ageing Shackleton fleet in working order. *(Robbie Shaw)*

and France). Its main drawback was that the air picture available to the fighter controller could be several minutes old under certain circumstances; this problem is solved by IUKADGE, which provides a real-time picture of the UK Air Defence Region — a vital asset if long-range cruise missiles are to be identified and intercepted.

After further project work by Systems Designers Ltd, a quality software company, together with considerable inputs by the Royal Air Force and the Royal Signals and Radar Establishment at Malvern, a £150 million fixed-price contract for the new system was awarded in September 1980 to UKADGE Systems Ltd, a consortium of Hughes Aircraft, Marconi and Plessey, each with one-third share. The digital data and voice communications network, known as Uniter, was developed by GEC under a separate contract.

IUKADGE involves three different types of new-generation radar, operating in two wavebands. There are two General Electric GE592 and four Marconi Martello 23 cm radars, operating in L-band, and six Plessey/ITT 10 cm radars operating in the S-band. All are three-dimensional radars capable of measuring target range, bearing and height. Each radar is deployed in a convoy of about fifteen vehicles to a pre-surveyed but unmarked site indistinguishable from the surrounding countryside. The radar head is located remotely from its associated reporting post, and is protected by decoys intended to confuse anti-radar missiles. The overlapping L-and S-band coverage also reduces the risk of enemy jamming. As an extra insurance, an electronic counter-counter measures officer forms part of the RP trailer crew, his function to assist the radar in overcoming any jamming problems. Associated with four of the twelve RPs — in the Faeroes, at Saxa Vord in the Shetlands, Benbecula in the Outer Hebrides and Portreath in Cornwall — are hardened Command and Reporting Posts (CRPs) with local tracking and fighter control capability; these provide backup facilities for the hardened CRCs, which are responsible under normal circumstances for tracking and interceptor control and which are the nerve centres of the UK air defence system. There are four of them, at Buchan, north of Aberdeen, Boulmer in Northumberland, Neatishead in Norfolk and Ash, on the Channel coast. Buchan and Neatishead are also Sector Operations Centres.

The process of building up a picture of a possible air threat begins with the first receipt of radar plots (target positions) and strobes (jammer bearings). This information is injected into the IUKADGE network via a narrow-band datalink. At the CRC, the plots are combined with those of other radars for multi-radar target tracking; those active tracks are then combined with passive tracks derived from jamming strobes. Tracks from airborne early warning and interceptor aircraft are also introduced, together with those from other CRCs, and track-to-track correlation is carried out to produce the local air picture. Then the recognition process begins, an automatic interface with West Drayton air traffic control centre ensuring instant access to all currently filed civil flight plans. Other SOC/CRCs supply track identities which help build the local recognised air picture. With the threat revealed, the fighter controllers can now marshal and direct their forces. Sea tracks are introduced into the system to produce the final recognised air-sea picture; this mutual exchange of information between elements ensures that all centres share the same constantly updated picture of the UK Air Defence Region, so that even if an element is lost, the big picture will remain intact. In addition, the CRCs interface with NADGE and France's Strida II air defence systems for target data exchange, with Royal Navy vessels assigned to air defence, and with E-3 AWACS aircraft.

IUKADGE is one part of a comprehensive air defence system which, by the time it is fully deployed in 1991, will have cost around £10 billion. Apart from the new radar and communications network, it includes, at a cost of £100 million, a new four-storey underground bunker at High Wycombe, which will house 800 personnel in a building hardened to withstand anything less than a direct hit from a nuclear missile for up to a week. When it is completed the system will be the most modern in the world and, for the first time since the Second World War, will bring together all the different elements of Britain's air defence under one umbrella. But there have been several costly obstacles *en route*.

## Airborne Early Warning

The requirement for a Royal Air Force airborne early warning (AEW) system dates back to the discontinuation of the Royal Navy's attack carriers, which were equipped with the Fairey Gannet AEW.3, and the assumption of fleet protection duties by the RAF. British experience with AEW began in the mid-1950s when Elliot Brothers (later Marconi Avionics) were called in to vet the US APS-20 radar, licence manufacture of which was planned to equip the RN AEW Gannets. In the event this equipment was purchased direct from the USA, with Marconi Avionics acting as UK support company. Later, when the APS-20 was selected to equip RAF Shackletons, Marconi Avionics became responsible for improving and updating the radar.

By the mid-1960s, trials with advanced strike aircraft such as the TSR-2 and with the V-Force, which had now assumed a low-level role, made it apparent that the APS-20 was not advanced enough to cope with the low-level threat. A requirement for a Gannet replacement (Naval Air Staff Target 6166) was formulated in 1964, and a four-month study was carried out on a future carrier-based AEW aircraft with fore and aft antennae, but the decision to phase out the carriers was made before work could progress. The RAF and RN jointly pursued studies of an AEW radar system that could be carried in a land-based aircraft; these led to project definition in 1968, and although further work was abandoned in 1970 because of the high technical risk and cost, Hawker Siddeley (later British Aerospace) and Marconi Avionics drew up a number of options based on HS 748 and Nimrod airframes, using planned and existing radars. The most promising of these at the time appeared to be to equip the Nimrod, which had plenty of capacity for displays and avionics, with the APS-125 rotodome radar used by the Grumman E-2C Hawkeye AEW aircraft. A further option was to equip Nimrod with Marconi Avionics AEW radar installed in fore and aft scanners.

In the meantime, to fill the AEW gap, it was decided to convert twelve Shackleton MR.Mk. 2 aircraft to the AEW role by equipping them with the APS-20 radar mounted in a large radome under the forward fuselage. The aircraft were to be operated from RAF Kinloss (and later Lossiemouth) at No. 8 Squadron, formerly a Hunter fighter/ground attack unit which disbanded at Sharjah in December 1971. Reformed immediately at Kinloss, No. 8 Squadron operated Shackleton MR. 2s from January to April 1972 to work up operational techniques before receiving the first of its AEW.2s in April. No. 8 Squadron's original operational task was to provide AEW coverage for Royal Navy vessels operating in the eastern Atlantic, but as the development of a new AEW aircraft for the RAF became more complex and protracted they were gradually absorbed into the UK air defence system. By 1981 a combination of airframe fatigue and economic considerations had reduced the original twelve aircraft to six, but these were still operating from Lossiemouth in 1989.

The lack of an advanced AEW capability was a problem common to the whole of European NATO, including Great Britain. In the 1970s, discussions began between the Alliance and the United States for the acquisition of eighteen Boeing E-3A Sentry Airborne Warning and Control System (AWACS) aircraft. Based at Geilenkirchen in the German Federal Republic, these would be manned by NATO crews and be under the control of the NATO AEW Force commander based at Supreme Headquarters Allied Powers Europe at Casteau, near Mons in Belgium. The Force Commander would receive tasks from the Supreme Allied Commander Europe (SACEUR) as the executive agency, and from Supreme Allied Commander Altantic (SAC-LANT) and Commander in Chief Channel (CINCCHAN).

The British Government was involved in these negotiations, which were beset by a number of obstacles, not least of which was the Alliance's insistence on improvements which were to include better overwater detection performance, funded by the USAF, and an increased capacity, high-speed computer, paid for by NATO. By 1976 there was considerable doubt whether the AWACS purchase would ever take place at all, and so the British Ministry of Defence authorised continued work on a backup programme; apart from any other consideration, it seemed politically, technically and economically desirable that a British project should be supported as an AWACS alternative. In March 1977, with the other NATO

In open storage at Abingdon are some of the ill-fated Nimrod AEW3s. A few have already been cannibalised for spares then scrapped. *(Robbie Shaw)*

Overleaf: Since the introduction of the Tornado F3 the Phantom fleet has been reduced and only two front line squadrons remain in No. 11 Group; Nos. 56 and 74. A pair of aircraft from the latter unit are illustrated.
*(Robbie Shaw)*

members still wrangling over who was to fund what in the AWACS programme and a number of operational aspects still unresolved, the British Government announced that the Nimrod AEW was to be developed, with an in-service target date of mid-1982, under Air Staff Requirement 400.

It seemed a sensible decision. The RAF would have its own force of eleven Nimrod AEW aircraft, their systems compatible with those of the NATO AWACS; eventually, with the introduction of the JTIDS (Joint Tactical Information Distribution System) secure, ECM-resistant data link, NATO would have a fully interoperable air defence system linking aircraft, ships and ground stations of different types. In the meantime, the Nimrods would enter service with an interim data link like that installed in the AWACS; AEW

The Phantom Operational Conversion Unit at Leuchars, No. 228, would in time of tension become 64 Squadron. One of its aircraft is seen here in a tight bank over the North Sea.
*(Robbie Shaw)*

Nimrod would be able to transfer data to the UK air defence ground environment and to any aircraft, ship or ground station equipped with a translator to handle the data link code.

At first, all went well. An aerodynamic trials airframe — a converted Comet 4C — flew in June 1977 and was followed by three development aircraft, two to prove the systems and the third for service trials to ensure that the aircraft met all the provisions of ASR.400. It was then that the problems started, throwing the whole Nimrod AEW schedule into disarray.

The first major problem involved the transmitter, which had to be redesigned. A power snag in the high-voltage transmitter led to inadvertent shutdowns and run-ups, which in turn caused noise greater than the ground clutter noise that the radar was designed to handle. The redesigned transmitter was running by the summer of 1984, and the next eighteen months were spent in getting to grips with the signal processing involved in picking out targets and tracking them against clutter. In fact, this was to absorb most of the development work from now on in a programme which, by the beginning of 1986, was already five years behind schedule and bogged down in major negotiations between GEC Avionics, makers of the Nimrod's radar and electronics system, and the Ministry of Defence. The Nimrod AEW project had now cost the taxpayer £882 million, and even if the radar problems were sorted out it was likely to be another four years before the aircraft became fully operational.

Amid a flurry of acrimonious publicity, GEC Avionics accused the MoD of altering the requirements of ASR.400 and therefore being partly to blame for the problems. The MoD, on the other hand, insisted that the original requirement had not changed in any significant way; only minor adjustments had been made, and none without discussion. The requirement was for AEW coverage over the northern flank, which meant over the North Sea, occasionally sweeping over coastal areas. The requirement had not been modified to include any overland capability.

By now the Royal Air Force was already pressing the UK Defence Minister, George Younger, to scrap the Nimrod AEW programme and buy six Boeing E-3s instead (the requirement was later increased to seven aircraft). The eighteen NATO AWACS were now in service and proving their worth, with individual aircraft deployed to the UK from time to time to exercise with the air defences. In December 1986 the RAF had its way at last: an order was placed for the E-3 and the AEW Nimrod was axed.

Major assembly of the first E-3 AWACS for the Royal Air Force was under way at Renton, near Seattle, at the end of 1988, and rollout took place in July 1989. The first aircraft had its mission avionics installed by Boeing; all subsequent installation and checkout work is being carried out by British Aerospace at RAF Waddington, which will be the main RAF AWACS operating base. The operating unit will be No. 8 Squadron, which will stand down from its alert commitment at RAF Lossiemouth at midnight on 30 June 1991 and immediately assume its new alert commitment at RAF Waddington with the Sentry AEW Mk. 1.

The UK AWACS is powered by four General Electric Snecma CFM56-2 turbofans and is fitted with a flight refuelling probe above and to the right of the flight deck. It is equipped with JTIDS and features the RAF's own electronic support measures (ESM) system developed for the Nimrod AEW, rather than the ESM upgrade being developed for the USAF and NATO AEW agency by Boeing. Deliveries of the UK AWACS are due within a twelve-month period beginning in January 1991, nearly a decade after the ill-starred AEW Nimrod was to have made its service debut.

## The Interceptors

Radar problems of a different kind also dogged the service trials of the aircraft that forms the spearhead of the UK air defences, the Panavia Tornado Air Defence Variant (ADV). The Tornado ADV is the product of Air Staff Target 395, issued in 1971, and calling for a minimum-change, minimum-cost, but effective interceptor to replace the British Aerospace Lightning F.6 and, in part, the F.4 Phantom in the air defence of the United Kingdom and the Fleet. Primary armament was to be the British Aerospace Dynamics XJ521 Sky Flash medium-range air-to-air missile, and the primary sensor a Marconi Avionics pulse-Doppler AI radar.

The original Tornado ADV study envisaged four Sky Flash missiles under the wings, long-range tanks under the fuselage and a modified nose to accommodate the AI radar. Early aerodynamic trials, however, showed that with pylon-mounted missiles the ADV's performance fell short of requirements, giving little or no advantage over that of the Phantom it was intended to replace, even allowing for further engine developments. The answer was to carry the AAMs semi-submerged under the fuselage, providing a low-drag configuration. To accommodate the front pair of missiles some lengthening of the forward fuselage was necessary, but this produced an added bonus in that it increased internal fuel capacity by ten per cent. A further armament change involved the deletion of one of the ADV's two planned Mauser 27 mm cannon, providing more space for the installation of avionics. The overall structural changes involved stretching the fuselage by 136 cm; the wing root glove was also given increased sweep, moving the centre of pressure forward to compensate for the resultant change of centre of gravity and to reduce wave drag.

Because of the minimum-change requirement, the only changes permitted to the Tornado IDS weapon system were those that would produce an effective air defence aircraft at minimum cost. First of all, this involved the removal of all equipment not required for the air defence role, including the Texas Instruments terrain-following/ground-mapping radar. The next stage was to identify equiment that only required modification to perform the air defence role. This included the Command Stability Augmentation System (CSAS), which required inputs to reduce stick pitch forces and increase roll rates for air combat. The result was a system common to both Tornado ADV and IDS, with the air defence equipment added. This comprised the Marconi Avionics AI radar, with integrated Cossor IFF interrogator, Singer-Kearfott secure datalink, Marconi Space and Defence Systems radar homing and warning receiver, Smiths Industries/Computing Devices missile management system, and a new electronic head-down display in the front cockpit. All this required a considerable re-write of the main computer software and resulted in more changes than had originally been envisaged, and each step was approved separately by the MoD, which considered a number of possible alternatives — including the F-14 and F-15 — before finally approving the whole ADV project in 1976.

The aircraft that eventually emerged was a long-range interceptor, with long on-CAP time, capable of engaging multiple targets in rapid succession, in all weathers and in complex ECM conditions. It was designed to operate with UKADGE, AEW aircraft, tankers and air defence ships, all linked in due course on a secure ECM-resistant data and voice command and control net. The problem of navigation at extreme range from fixed navigation systems was overcome by a highly accurate twin inertial platform, the Ferranti FIN1010, which provided the computer with accurate position data for steering to a large number of fixed or moving positions. This could be done automatically by use of the autopilot, allowing the crew to concentrate on the tactical information provided by the AI radar and datalink.

The crew of an F-4J of 74 'Tiger' Squadron. *(Robbie Shaw)*

The intercept radar selected for the Tornado ADV was the Marconi (later GEC) Avionics AI.24 Foxhunter. The essential requirement was that detection ranges should in no way be limited by target altitude. Look-down capability against low-level targets was the most demanding case, particularly when the interceptor itself was at low altitude. Severe and sophisticated electronic countermeasures also had to be overcome. Development of the radar began in 1974.

By the time the first Tornado ADV was ready to fly, late in 1979, its external stores fit had also undergone changes. The four Sky Flash AAMs were now joined by four AIM-9L Sidewinders on underwing stations, and the capacity of each drop tank increased from 1,500 litres to 2,250 litres to extend unrefuelled range and time on CAP.

Three Tornado ADV prototypes were built. All were powered by the Turbo-Union RB.199 Mk. 103 turbofan, which was also to power the initial production batch of Tornado F.2s for the RAF. These aircraft also featured manually-controlled wing sweep, which would be automatic on later production aircraft. The first development Tornado ADV, A01, was a single-stick aircraft assigned to handling, performance and general systems evaluation. Early in 1982, to demonstrate that the ADV could fulfil its CAP requirements in all respects, this aircraft flew a CAP of two hours twenty minutes over the North Sea, involving a flight of 325 nm to the CAP area and a similiar return flight. The aircraft was climbed out of Warton and cruised at high altitude across the North Sea, then descended to medium altitude to take up a CAP racetrack pattern. On arriving back at base the aircraft loitered in the local area for fifteen minutes at low level before landing with more than five per cent internal fuel remaining after a total flight time of four hours thirteen minutes.

It was a very promising indication of the ADV's capability. So were the armament trials, carried out by A02 in the same year. Sky Flash firings were carried out from 0.9M into the supersonic envelope, while Mauser gun firing trials covered the subsonic flight envelope above 200 knots from zero g to the angle of attack limit, and up to 30,000 feet. By the end of 1982, A03 had done most of the necessary radar and weapon system integration flight trials, and pre-production radar flight trials were scheduled to start in the near future — although it was now apparent that deliveries of the operational AI.24 were going to be alarmingly late.

A 74 Squadron F-4J guzzling fuel from a VC-10 tanker. The unit is proud to be a 'Tiger' squadron, hence the colourful and distinctive markings on the crew's helmets. *(Robbie Shaw)*

Nevertheless, there was nothing wrong with the aircraft and its other systems, and RAF orders now stood at 165, to be delivered in three batches. Pilots of 'A' Squadron, A&AEE, Boscombe Down, who evaluated it, were very enthusiastic about all aspects except the radar, which failed to meet its specification in no fewer than fifty-two areas.

The problems with the Foxhunter were still far from resolved when the first Tornado F.2s were delivered to No. 229 Operational Conversion Unit at RAF Coningsby, in Lincolnshire, in November 1984. The first eighteen aircraft were all powered by Mk. 103 engines; aircraft after that had the more powerful Mk. 104, which combines a 360 mm reheat extension with a Lucas Aerospace digital electronic engine control unit (DECU). These later aircraft, designated Tornado F.3, also feature the full armament of four Sky Flash and four AIM-9Ls, auto wing sweep, and automanoeuvre devices with the slats and flaps deploying as a function of angle-of-attack and wing sweep.

It was not until 1986 that the first modified AI.24 Foxhunter radars were delivered for installation in the OCU aircraft;

the modifications had cost an additional £250 million. By this time the Foxhunter had received the nickname of 'Blue Circle', bestowed because of the need to ballast the aircraft's nose with blocks of cement to compensate for the missing AI equipment. With the snags largely ironed out, however, Tornado navigators quickly became as enthusiastic as the pilots.

'Navigation is easy. We are now mission managers or systems operators. The AI.24 is very good, very ECM-resistant, and the look-down capability is streets ahead of anything the RAF has had before. We can do raid sorting on aircraft we would have been lucky to see before. The multiple track-while-scan mode is a terrific advantage in a multi-bogey environment. Knowing where all the players are makes all the difference.'

How, then, does the Tornado F.3 fit into the RAF's present and future air defence system, and how well can it cope with the likely air threat? The first squadron, No. 29, formed at RAF Coningsby in

Top left: You can almost feel the power as the afterburners propel this Tornado F3 down the runway. The aircraft is from 65 (Shadow) Squadron 229 OCU. *(Robbie Shaw)*
Above left: As well as being home to 229 OCU, Coningsby is host to two operational F3 squadrons: Nos. 5 and 29. This 'twin-stick' trainer Tornado F3 belongs to 5 Squadron. *(Robbie Shaw)*
Opposite: Dusk patrol; a Tornado F3 highlighted as night approaches. *(Gordon Scott)*

May 1987 and was declared operational at the end of October. Four more squadrons out of a planned total of seven had also formed on the Tornado F.3 by the end of 1989; these were No. 5 Squadron at RAF Coningsby and Nos. 11, 23 and 25 Squadrons at RAF Leeming. The latter base, in North Yorkshire, will be the largest Tornado F.3 establishment, with a wing of three squadrons. Other squadrons converting in 1990 to the F.3 are Nos. 43 and 111 at RAF Leuchars in Scotland, which in 1989 were operating a mixture of Phantom FGR.2s and FG.1s. This will leave RAF Wattisham, in Suffolk, as No. 11 Group's only air defence Phantom base, with Nos. 56 and 74 Squadrons, the latter operating ex-US Navy F-4Js.

The Tornado F.3 has opened up a whole new range of tactical possibilities for No. 11 Group. It has excellent take-off and landing characteristics, which means that — together with the Auxiliary Power Unit and datalink — the aircraft can, if necessary, deploy to small airfields or even sections of motorway. All the crew needs to do is to remain on cockpit alert, monitoring tactical developments on the multi-function displays via the datalink, and wait for the order to scramble. Even before the battle is joined, pilot and navigator will have an accurate appraisal of the tactical situation.

Normal operations with the Tornado F.3 involve what is known as a 'heavy combat fit', which means four Sky Flash, four Sidewinders and no external tanks. CAP fit with the two tanks is reserved specifically for long-range sorties. A good example of what the F.3 can achieve without the long-range tanks was shown on 10 September 1988, when two aircraft of No. 5 Squadron were scrambled from Coningsby to intercept a pair of Tupolev Tu-95 Bear-D maritime radar reconnaissance aircraft over the Norwegian Sea. A VC-10 tanker was scrambled from RAF Leuchars to rendezvous with the Tornados, which carried out the intercept successfully. Normally, intercepts over the Norwegian Sea were carried out by the Leuchars-based Phantoms.

The Tornado F.3 is, first and foremost, a missile platform. The aircraft's AI.24 radar uses a technique known as frequency modulated interrupted continuous wave (FMICW), with which is integrated a Cossor IFF-3500 interrogator and a radar signal processor to suppress ground clutter (which, in fact, was one of the major problems associated with its lengthy development). The radar's high pulse repetition frequency (PRF) enables it to detect targets at an initial range of about 100 nm, while FMICW allows the range of the target to be determined from the frequency change between transmission and reception.

As they are detected, the targets are stored in the Central Digital Computer (which is the same as that in the IDS variant). Since the radar continues to scan normally, the targets are unaware that they are the subject of detailed analysis. The system rejects unwanted signals, leaving only real targets which then pass through the radar data processor prior to display to the aircraft's crew. While the radar keeps up a 'running commentary' on ranges, velocities and tracks of established targets, it continues to scan and report new plots.

With the computer fully updated, the crew plan their approach to engage the maximum number of targets. Displays are duplicated in the front cockpit for the pilot, who steers to the engagement on his head-up display (HUD). The symbology for Sky Flash, Sidewinder or gun attacks is very clear, and an important feature is the target indicator which aids the pilot in an early visual sighting.

For a long-range interception, the Sky Flash semi-active radar homing AAM would be used. This weapon was developed from the AIM-7E Sparrow, already in use on RAF air defence Phantoms, and features six areas of improvement: early discrimination between grouped targets; positive target detection and tracking against radar ground clutter; ECM resistance; more accurate guidance resulting in reduced miss distance; better proximity fuzing; and improved reliability. It has a range of around 30 nm. The missile will eventually be replaced by Active Sky Flash; this will have a Marconi Defence Systems radar homing head, eliminating the present need for continuous-wave illumination by the firing aircraft's radar all the way to the target.

Sky Flash is integrated with the aircraft's radar system, being tuned to search in the correct frequency band via its rear reference aerial. The Foxhunter radar illuminates the target scene, and when a hostile is identified within that scene Sky Flash is ready for launch. As Foxhunter continues to illuminate the target, the reflected radar signals are received by the missile seeker; signals sent by the aircraft are received through the missile's rear reference aerial and are corrected for Doppler shift so that Sky Flash homes on to the correct target. The seeker can separate a close formation of aircraft into individuals and select one for attack; this prevents it from becoming confused and missing all of them, which has been a drawback with earlier generations of AAMs.

The missile launch sequence lasts less than a tenth of a second, the missile being driven down from its fuselage recess by two gas-operated, long-stroke rams (developed by Frazer-Nash) through the flow fields around the aircraft. Additonally, the rams stabilise the missile in roll and yaw during ejection, and are then retracted to avoid adding post-launch drag. This system enables the F.3 to launch its missiles across the entire flight envelope.

For engagements at closer range the AIM-9L Sidewinder would be used. To respond quickly to a close-in threat, the pilot can take control of the radar and weapons systems by selecting the air-to-air override mode. This mode, optimised for visual combat, is controlled by two multi-function buttons mounted on the throttle. Pressing the buttons in sequence selects the close combat radar mode and associated HUD displays, as well as the required weapons, without the pilot having to take his hands off the throttle or stick. Compared with the long and difficult reach to the armament panel in a Phantom, the system is very easy to use. A hand controller, located aft of the throttles, may be used to slew the radar scanner or missile homing heads if the automatic HUD scan pattern is insufficient to acquire the target. Once the target is in scan, lock-on is automatic.

In due course, the AIM-9L will probably be replaced by the latest version, the AIM-9R, which should be operational in the early 1990s. The AIM-9R will have greater acquisition range and improved ECCM performance; like the 9L it will be virtually immune to flares due to filtering of the tracker, but it will also be able to resist IR jammers which attempt to defeat the missile's seeker by breaking its lock-on with a rapidly alternating IR signal from an electrically-heated ceramic panel. Other missile options for the Tornado F.3 in the future are the AIM-120A AMRAAM and the AIM-132 ASRAAM, the latter envisaged as a Sidewinder replacement. However, although the former — designed to replace the Sparrow — was already in production in 1990 and equipping the Royal Navy's Sea Harrier FRS.2s, the latter, dogged by development and political difficulties in the European consortium responsible for it (the UK, Norway and Germany), had yet to leave the drawing board.

Although not a fighter in the strictest sense of the word, the Tornado F.3 gives an excellent account of itself in combat with other contemporary aircraft, including the F-16 Fighting Falcon. With its wing swept at forty-five degrees the Tornado can hold its own in a turning fight with anything in service today, with the possible exception of the Harrier family. The aircraft's Spin Prevention and Incidence Limiting System (SPILS) provides carefree handling, and stick forces are about thirty per cent lighter than those of the Tornado GR.1. Another useful feature is that the pilot can bang the throttles open and shut without penalty. The F.3 is capable of 2.2M at high level, and more than 800 knots at low level; in both cases fuel consumption is surprisingly low. Clean-wing endurance is about the same as that of a Phantom with its tanks on; a 'clean' Tornado F.3 can fly for one hour at 420 knots, low-level, and still have half an hour's worth of fuel left.

Taking all the aircraft's attributes into account, together with possible future modifications to airframe, engines and equipment, there seems little doubt that the Tornado F.3 will adequately fulfil its air defence task for at least the next ten to fifteen years. In dealing with the air threat, it must also be remembered that the Tornados, positioned as far north as possible in a war situation, would be operating in concert with considerable numbers of other NATO types such as the F-15 Eagle (from Keflavik in Iceland), and F-14 Tomcats and F-18 Hornets (from USN carriers). The whole force would be well placed and equipped to deal with saturation attacks, which in the early stages would probably be directed against NATO naval forces in the Norwegian Sea and the Iceland-Faeroes Gap.

Below: Low and fast with lots of noise! A Tornado F3 of 65 (Shadow) Squadron 229 OCU with wings swept performs an airshow flypast. *(Robbie Shaw)*

Opposite: This view of a Tornado F3 of 65 (Shadow) Squadron shows the forward recesses for the Sky Flash missiles. *(Robbie Shaw)*

The biggest threat to the United Kingdom itself, however, would come if the enemy seized forward airfields in NATO territory — Norway, for example — enabling shorter-range combat aircraft to attack UK targets. Enemy forces operating out of Norway would almost certainly mean that NATO had lost the Battle of the Norwegian Sea. In this eventuality, the outer layer of the UK air defence system, which effectively means the Tornados, would have to be pulled in more tightly to integrate with other RAF air defence elements — the whole forming the operational concept known as the Mixed Fighter Force.

### The Mixed Fighter Force

The concept of the Mixed Fighter Force, with missile-armed British Aerospace Hawks forming a second line of defence, dates back to 1979, when it was announced in parliament that the Hawk, armed with the AIM-9L Sidewinder AAM, was to be introduced to plug the gap in the UK air defences. The possibility of forming a third squadron of Lightnings to join the two already operational at RAF Binbrook (Nos. 5 and 11) was considered, but this scheme was later dropped.

The Hawk War Role Programme, as it was known, went ahead under the joint auspices of the Ministry of Defence Procurement Executive, the RAF and British Aerospace. The aim was to give eighty-nine Hawks, whose sole armament then was a 30 mm Aden gun, an air defence capability by fitting two Sidewinder stations to each aircraft. Development was started early in 1980, and as work progressed two important modifications were added to the air defence installation programme: the fitting of strobe lights and a twin gyro platform to provide a high accuracy attitude reference system.

The first Sidewinder was fired in 1980 and, after some problems caused by the effect of the missile smoke trail had been satisfactorily resolved, a useful AIM-9L Sidewinder firing envelope was released for use by the Service in May 1983. By this time British Aerospace had been awarded a contract (on 31 January 1983) for the modification of eighty-nine Hawks to War Role standard for the second-line defence of UK installations. Aircraft so modified — those in service with Nos. 1 and 2 Tactical Weapons Units at RAF Brawdy and RAF Chivenor, together with those of the Central Flying School at RAF Scampton (including the aircraft used by the Red Arrows) — were allocated the designation Hawk T.Mk 1A.

The modification programme was completed in August 1986, by which time the original concept of using the missile-armed Hawks for point defence had undergone changes as a result of lessons learned during air defence exercises. The original idea had been to deploy the first line of defence — the F.3 Tornado and the F.4 Phantom — as far forward as possible, using tankers if necessary. The second line would be provided by the Bloodhound SAMs, with short-range Rapier SAMs and the Hawks forming the last line. This plan assumed, of course, that the RAF's air defence and strike airfields were the enemy's principal targets; as the Hawk is not equipped with radar, it would fly combat air patrol (CAP) on the threat axis, as far from the airfield as possible but within the airfield's radar cover.

The major problem with this scheme was one of warning time. In a real war situation there would almost certainly be gaps in the continental NATO radar and C³ (Command, Control and Communications) chain, so that there might be little or no advance warning of incoming enemy aircraft in the absence of AWACS or AD (Air Defence) ships at sea operating in the fighter-direction role. As a Hawk pilot on airfield CAP would rely on advance warning to determine any changes to the threat axis, and then on his eyesight to detect incoming hostiles, the arrangement was clearly unsatisfactory.

The Hawk T.1A's original task of acting independently on a day visual CAP of an airfield was therefore reduced to a secondary role; the primary role, as part of the Mixed Fighter Force, is now to operate in concert with either Phantoms or Tornado F.3s, the idea being to catch the enemy as far out as possible. Each Phantom or Tornado flies in company with one or two Hawks in loose formation; the threat is detected by AWACS, AD vessel (A Type 42 destroyer, for example), ground radar or the aircraft's own AI radar. The Tornado or Phantom then uses its radar to set up the engagement and, because of the threat of severe jamming, uses visual signals to alert the Hawk. As soon as radar contact is established the Phantom/Tornado waggles its wings — the pilot actually stands the aircraft on one wingtip and then rolls it around its axis to stand on the other — and the Hawk pilot replies in similar fashion by way of acknowledgement. Depending on the Rules of Engagement in force at the time, the Tornado/Phantom might be in a position to launch its long-range missiles, in which case the first clue the Hawk pilot might have that a hostile has been detected is when he sees the smoke trails. Either way, the Tornado/Phantom pilot then heads directly for the threat and the Hawk goes along with him.

If the incoming hostiles were to consist of bombers with a fighter escort, the Hawks would take on the fighters while the more heavily-armed aircraft went for the bombers. Once this happened the Hawks would be on their own; after the fight, assuming that they had weapons and fuel remaining, they would return to the CAP and loiter, teaming up with whoever else arrived in the event that their original companions needed to return to base to refuel and rearm. The total flexibility of the MFF scheme allows a mixed CAP of Tornados, Phantoms and Hawks to operate effectively together.

In its fighter role the Hawk T.1A enjoys a number of distinct advantages. It is extremely agile, has a small radar signature and its engine is smoke-free, which means that it stands a very good chance of detecting a hostile aircraft visually and beginning an engagement before the hostile pilot realises that it is there. Tactical Weapons Unit Hawks have proven their combat ability on numerous occasions during detachments to the Air Combat Manoeuvring Instrumentation (ACMI) training range at Deccimommannu in Sardinia, where they have been pitted against heavier and more sophisticated aircraft such as the F-15 Eagle.

Their main limitation in the Mixed Fighter Force role is that they are restricted to day only operations, and in war conditions a high proportion of hostile sorties would be flown at night. The concept of the Mixed Fighter Force is good, and has shown itself in practice to be workable, but to be fully effective the close-in fighter element would need to be able to operate at night and in weather conditions where purely visual detection and engagement would be impossible.

If the MFF concept is to continue, then the Hawk T.1A element needs to be supplemented by another aircraft which can engage hostile aircraft at night and in marginal weather. The obvious answer is the single-seat Hawk 200, an aircraft which, while remaining as rugged and simple to maintain as its stablemates, takes the basic design a whole generation further forward. The Hawk 200 is equipped with the Westinghouse AN/APG-66 pulse doppler multi-mode radar, which permits totally autonomous target detection and engagement. In the airspace denial role — only one of several missions the aircraft can undertake — it carries two Sidewinder-type AAMs and has a built-in armament of either one or two high velocity 25 mm Aden guns. At 30,000 feet, with this armament and two 190 Imp gal (860 litre) drop tanks, it can remain on station for three and a half hours at 100 nm from base, two hours at 375 nm and one hour at 550 nm. Its maximum intercept radius is 720 nm. Other performance figures include a maximum dive speed of 1.2M, a maximum level speed of 560 knots, and a maximum altitude of 50,000 feet. The aircraft is stressed to plus 8g and minus 4g, load factors which give it a considerable advantage in a turning fight.

The Hawk 200 was designed from the outset to be a cost-effective, multi-role combat aircraft. In RAF service it could readily be switched from one role to another, providing additional assets to meet a prevailing threat. For example, in the close support role, with one 130 gal (590 litre) external fuel tank, it can lift eight 500 lb bombs over a lo-lo combat radius of 174 nm, or five 1,000 lb and four 500 lb over 104 nm; in the interdictor role, with two 190 gal (860 litre) fuel tanks, it has a hi-lo-hi radius of 579 nm with a 3,000 lb warload; in the lo-lo reconnaissance role, with two 190 gal (860 litre) and one 130 gal (590 litre) fuel tanks, its radius is 510 nm; and in the anti-shipping role, armed with two Sea Eagle missiles and carrying two 190 gal external fuel tanks, it has a very respectable hi-hi radius of 800 nm.

The requirement for a 'close-in' fighter will still exist even when the European Fighter Aircraft begins to enter RAF service in the air defence role some time after 1995. The EFA will replace the Phantom and will be based in southern England — probably at Coltishall and Wattisham — to provide air defence cover of the

Below: An 11 Squadron Tornado F3 seen off the coast of Stornoway, a location the unit frequently operates from. *(Robbie Shaw)*

Opposite: A final check from the groundcrew prior to applying power to leave the hardened shelter. This Tornado F3 belongs to No. 25 Squadron at Leeming. *(Robbie Shaw)*

Channel and the southern North Sea, releasing most of the Tornado F.3 force to intercept enemy aircraft trying to break through to the North Atlantic convoy routes (and to vital installations in the northern sectors of the British Isles) and also to provide fighter cover for NATO naval forces in the Norwegian Sea.

## The European Fighter Aircraft

The Royal Air Force Operational Requirements Branch began planning for a next-generation fighter to replace the F-4 Phantom in the air defence role, and the Jaguar in the offensive support role, in October 1981. The need crystallized in Staff Requirement (Air) 414, which specified a short-range highly agile air defence/offensive support aircraft, and the project that filled the requirement was the European Fighter Aircraft (EFA).

The EFA programme is managed by the NATO European Fighter Management Agency (NEFMA), which lets contracts to Eurofighter, a four-nation partnership comprising Aeritalia of Italy, British Aerospace, CASA of Spain, and MBB and Dornier of Germany, acting in collusion. To prove the necessary technology, a contract was awarded in May 1983 to British Aerospace for the development of an agile demonstrator aircraft — not a prototype — under the heading Experimental Aircraft Programme, or EAP. The cost was to be shared between the partner companies of the EFA consortium and the UK Ministry of Defence.

The EAP demonstrator flew for the first time on 8 August 1986, only three years after the programme was conceived. Powered by two RB.199 Mk. 104D engines, it is the most advanced aircraft ever produced in Britain. A single-seat delta-canard aircraft, its design emphasis is on air combat performance, which in practice means a combination of high turn rates and high specific excess power — the measure of a fighter's ability to regain speed or altitude after a manoeuvre. The EAP's basic design owes a great deal to a project known as the Agile Combat Aircraft, which was jointly proposed in 1982 by the Panavia partners: British Aerospace, MBB and Aeritalia. No Government backing for the ACA was forthcoming, but the UK Ministry of Defence allocated £70 million in research and development funds to the EAP. In fact, the United Kingdom provided the only government support for the project; in December 1983 Aeritalia and MBB, which are both state-owned, were directed by their respective governments to withdraw from the programme. However, Aeritalia continued to contribute to the programme using its own funds, building one of the aircraft's

Below: The view from the rear seat of a 29 Squadron Tornado F3 as it refuels from a VC-10 tanker. *(Gordon Scott)*

Opposite: A Sidewinder equipped Hawk T1A of 151 Squadron on a low level CAP near its home base, Chivenor. *(Robbie Shaw)*

carbon fibre wings, and equipment suppliers in Germany and Italy also maintained an active involvement.

The result is a superb aircraft which, in effect, is the blueprint for the fighter that will form much of NATO's front line and project the Alliance's leading European air forces — including the RAF — into the 21st Century, providing the means to counter any foreseeable air threat. EFA's task will be to fight effectively throughout the combat spectrum, from engagements beyond visual range down to close-in combat; the technologies necessary to enable it to do this are so advanced, and in some cases so unique, that the role of the EAP demonstrator is vital to the EFA project as a whole.

In the air defence role, as soon as a hostile aircraft is detected beyond visual range, the EFA must accelerate from its CAP loiter as quickly as possible in order to give its medium-range, fire-and-forget missiles maximum launch energy, fire as soon as it is in range, and then manoeuvre hard without losing energy to force incoming enemy missiles to make violent course corrections near the end of their flight, reducing their chances of scoring hits. This phase of the engagement, therefore, requires high acceleration and good supersonic manoeuvrability.

The next phase — close-in combat — requires maximum usable lift and a high thrust-to-weight ratio, so that energy lost in turns can quickly be regained. In this phase the EFA will use all-aspect short-range weaponry, the engagement starting with fast head-on attacks and then breaking down into a turning fight, with pilots manoeuvring hard to acquire good firing positions quickly. The EFA's missiles will comprise the AIM-120 as the primary weapon, with the AIM-132 ASRAAM chosen as the secondary. The aircraft will also have a built-in gun armament, probably the 27 mm Mauser.

The EFA will be very much a pilot's aeroplane, with emphasis on the best possible all-round visibility and comfort during high-g manoeuvres. One big asset will be the pilot's helmet-mounted sight, avoiding the need to pull tight turns to achieve missile lock-on and consequently reduce the risk of g-induced loss of consciousness (G-loc). Pilots will also have a new, fast-reacting g-suit, the design of which is currently being studied by the Institute of Aviation Medicine at the Royal Aircraft Establishment, Farnborough. These innovations mean that there will be no need to rake the EFA's ejection seat at more than the conventional eighteen-degree angle, which is good from the visibility point of view. It also means that a centrally-positioned control column can be retained (aircraft with highly-raked seats, like the F-16, need a side-stick).

The cockpit itself will feature colour head-down multifunction displays and a wide-angle holographic HUD. Direct Voice Input (DVI) will control such items as radio channel changes or map displays, but not safety-critical systems such as undercarriage operation or weapon firing. The cockpit area will be relatively lightly armoured, providing protection against light-to-medium calibre AA; the heavy armour is reserved for the critical systems, the thinking being that it is more important to provide the pilot with additional defensive electronics than extra armour plate.

One of the most advanced and ambitious EFA systems is the Defensive Avionics Sub-System (DASS), which is designed to cope with the multiple and mass threats that would characterize a war on NATO's central front. The system, which is being developed by Eurodass — a four-nation consortium led by the UK's Marconi Defence Systems and comprising Electronica of Spain, AEG of Germany and Ensa and Inisel of Spain — combines and correlates outputs from EFA's radar warning receiver, laser detectors, and other sensors and then automatically triggers the best combination of active and passive defences while warning the pilot of the threat priority.

The question of the EFA's radar had not been resolved at the time of writing, but only two consortia were in the running. Ferranti, leading a European consortium, was offering the ECR.90, based on the Blue Vixen developed for the Sea Harrier FRS.2, while AEG was leading another consortium offering a radar based on Hughes Aircraft's APG-65 radar for the F-18 Hornet. The specification calls for long-range performance and small size; moreover, Eurofighter wants the radar delivered two years ahead of the aircraft, to avoid the kind of delay associated with the Tornado F.3's Foxhunter.

The first two EFA prototypes, P01 and P02, will be powered by an interim engine, the Turbo-Union RB.199-122, but the third prototype and subsequent EFAs will have two 20,000 lb thrust EJ.200s developed by Eurojet Turbo GmbH, a joint company comprising Fiat, MTU, Rolls-Royce and SENER. If the EFA programme runs to schedule, P01 will fly from Manching in 1991, followed by P02 from Warton three months later. Both of these will be used for aerodynamic and handling trials. P03 will be a two-seater and will fly from Warton three months after P02. The first Italian aircraft will be a single-seater P04, and will fly from Caselle in 1992. The first aircraft to have the full avionics fit will be P05, which will fly from Warton; P06 will fly from Manching and P07, the first aircraft assembled by Spain's CASA, will be the second two-seat prototype. The last, P08, will fly from Caselle. All eight will be flying within two years of P01's first flight, and the aim is to complete 2,000 hours of flight testing by the time the aircraft enters squadron service in mid-1996.

Following the precedent set with the Tornado GR.1, it is likely that a multi-national EFA training establishment will be formed, either at Coltishall or Lossiemouth, to standardize EFA pilots on ground-attack procedures, while the individual air forces train their air defence pilots in AD procedures appropriate to the requirements of their own operational theatres. In this case, the first RAF unit to receive the EFA will probably be No. 228 Operational Conversion Unit, which is currently the Phantom OCU.

## Surface-to-Air Missile Defences

The RAF's primary SAM system, under the operational control of No. 11 Group, is the Bloodhound Mk. 2. In its original version, Bloodhound was developed by the Bristol Aeroplane Company and Ferranti under the code name Red Duster, and was deployed in

1958-61 to defend the RAF's V-Force bases. Development of the Bloodhound Mk. 2 began in 1958; the new variant had a better performance, continuous-wave (CW) guidance and a capability against low-level targets. The whole Mk. 2 system was designed to be either portable or fixed-base, the portable system using the Ferranti Firelight target illuminating radar (TIR) and the fixed-base system the AEI Scorpion.

The Bloodhound SAM system has been frequently updated over the years to keep pace with the changing air threat. The last such update took place in 1987, when British Aerospace Naval and Electronic Systems Division completed installation of the first automated operations room for the Bloodhound squadrons in East Anglia, as part of the revised UK air defence system mentioned earlier in this chapter.

The Bloodhound Mk. 2 forms the last-but-one line of defence against an air threat coming in from the North Sea. It is deployed with No. 25 Squadron, which has sites at Barkston Heath, Wyton and Wattisham, and No. 85 Squadron, with sites at Bawdsey, West Raynham and North Coates. Each Bloodhound squadron has several flights, each with three or four launch control posts directing up to eight missile launchers. The advent of the automated operations rooms means that each squadron and flight is now linked with the others by computer; information presented to the control room operators on consoles is continuously updated and, if interconnecting land-lines are damaged in action or develop a fault, the equipment automatically finds an alternative communications link. A map of the UK air space defended by Bloodhound is displayed on a screen in each operations room, together with the positions and tracks of potential targets and the identities of the missile units capable of engaging them.

The two Leuchars based front line squadrons, Nos. 43 and 111, have relinquished Phantoms in favour of the Tornado F3. The first to do so was 43 'Fighting Cocks' Squadron, one of whose aircraft is illustrated. *(Robbie Shaw)*

Bloodhound is launched with the aid of four solid-fuel rocket boosters, which are jettisoned once the missile has reached sufficient velocity to allow two Rolls-Royce Bristol Thor ramjets to take over. Performance details are classified, but the missile accelerates to Mach two plus and has a slant range of about fifty miles (80 kilometres). Bloodhound is expected to be able to counter any likely air threat well into the 1990s, and at present no plans have been announced to replace it with another system. However, British Aerospace Dynamics have for some years been offering a land-based system of the well-proven Sea Dart (and later of the Lightweight Sea Dart, which consists of a fixed launcher with containerised rounds and a Marconi 805SD tracking-illuminating radar). Sea Dart has a Mach 3.5 cruise, a range about the same as Bloodhound's, and can engage targets at any altitude between 100 feet (thirty metres) and

82,500 feet (25,000 metres). The system will be viable until at least the year 2000; the deployment of Land Dart in some numbers, either in the twin- or single-launcher version on offer, would make a great deal of sense. Admittedly, Sea Dart is deployed on the air defence vessels that would be positioned in the North Sea in a war situation, but it is doubtful whether these vessels would last for long in the face of determined and massive enemy attacks.

The last line of defence in the UK system is the British Aerospace Rapier point-defence missile. An outstandingly successful weapon, it equips Nos. 27 and 48 Squadrons of the Royal Air Force Regiment at the key airfields of Leuchars and Lossiemouth, which would be among the first to come under threat in wartime, and also Nos. 19, 20 and 66 Squadrons of the RAF Regiment, which formed in the mid-1980s for the purpose of protecting vital USAF airfields in the United Kingdom. The parent unit is No. 6 Wing at RAF West Raynham, which is also the site of the RAF Rapier Training School. No. 66 Squadron is based at West Raynham, but in a war threat situation would deploy two flights to cover RAF Mildenhall and RAF Lakenheath; similarly, No. 19 Squadron would deploy from its base at Brize

A Sidewinder equipped Hawk T1A of 151 Squadron on a low level CAP near its home base, Chivenor. (Robbie Shaw)

Norton to guard RAF Upper Heyford and RAF Fairford, while No. 20 Squadron, based at Honington, has the task of covering RAF Alconbury and the twin bases at RAF Bentwaters and Woodbridge. Each RAF Regiment flight has four fire units, and under operational conditions these would be deployed in positions up to 7.5 miles (twelve kilometres) outside the airfield perimeter in order to engage their targets before the latter could reach a weapon release point.

The British forces have recently completed an update programme under which their Rapier systems were modified from the original Field Standard A to the improved Field Standard B1. Trials of the fully-digital Electro-Optical Rapier (known earlier as Darkfire) started in 1985; this introduced the Scorpio infra-red tracker which replaces the current optical tracking unit, a six-round towed launcher incorporating an improved Racal-Decca surveillance radar with fifty per cent more range, and a Console Tactical Control for the fire unit commander.

There is no doubt that Rapier will remain one of the UK air defence system's most valuable assets until well into the next century. Since 1986, the UK has been committed to spending £1,270 million on the development and initial production of the latest variant, Rapier 2000. Due to enter service in the early 1990s, it will equip two Royal Artillery air defence regiments and three squadrons of the RAF Regiment.

Rapier 2000 introduces an eight-round launcher with four launch rails per side and a steerable spherical housing for a Darkfire-style optronic tracker. This occupies the location used by the surveillance radar on current systems. Rapier 2000 uses a trailer-mounted Plessey 3D radar with a built-in IFF system, plus an updated version of the Blind-fire radar tracker which tracks both the target and the missile simultaneously at night and in adverse weather and is an addition to the daylight optical system.

The futuristic looking British Aerospace EAP. *(Robbie Shaw)*

The new system will fire the new Mk. 2 version of the Rapier missile, a round which remains compatible with existing launchers. Two versions are planned, the Mk. 2A with a fragmentation warhead and an active IR proximity fuse, and the Mk. 2B with a contact-fused hollow-charge warhead. The Mk. 2A will be able to engage small targets such as remotely-piloted vehicles (RPVs), anti-radiation missiles and cruise missiles, while the Mk. 2B will be used against strike aircraft and heavily-armoured attack helicopters. Rapier 2000, which is powered by an improved Royal Ordnance Thermopylae rocket motor, can fire two-round salvoes and has a range of up to five miles (eight kilometres).

# CHAPTER THREE
## No. 18 Group, Strike Command

No. 18 Group provides a very important element of Britain's maritime forces and, together with the Royal Navy and NATO allies, is responsible for the security of sea communications in the Atlantic, North Sea and home waters. With its fleet of Nimrod long-range maritime reconnaissance aircraft, the Group's principal peacetime task is to carry out continual surveillance operations in order to maintain a flow of information about the movements of potentially hostile surface vessels and submarines over vast ocean areas. The Group has a variety of other tasks, including search and rescue and rapid deployment to overseas locations in limited war situations, but its main activities are surveillance and operational training.

Much of the training is concerned with NATO, to which No. 18 Group's resources would be committed in time of war. In that event, the Group would be released to the operational control of the Supreme Allied Commander Atlantic (SACLANT), and the Air Officer Commanding No. 18 Group, with his HQ at Northwood in Middlesex, holds the NATO posts of Maritime Air Commander Channel Command (COMMAIRCHAN) and Maritime Air Commander Eastern Atlantic (COMMAIREASTLANT). The Naval Commander, who is both C-in-C Channel and C-in-C Eastern Atlantic, delegates command and control of all land-based maritime aircraft assigned to him to the Maritime Air Commander.

The main wartime tasks of these Commands would be reconnaissance, support of the Atlantic Striking Fleet, control, routing and protection of shipping and the conduct of offensive operations against enemy submarines and surface vessels.

The Group controls Northern Maritime Air Region at Pitreavie Castle, Fife, and Southern Maritime Air Region at Mount Wise, Devon. Units within the Group include the Maritime Reconnaissance Force; the Search and Rescue Organisation; the Northern and Southern Rescue Co-Ordination Centres; the RAF Element of the Joint Maritime Operational Training Staff (where naval and air force personnel train together); No. 236 Operational Training Unit; the School of Combat Survival and Rescue; and the Maritime Headquarters Units of the Royal Auxiliary Air Force.

## Resources

The principal asset of No. 18 Group is the British Aerospace Nimrod MR.2. Thirty-six of these aircraft equip No. 42 Squadron and No. 236 Operational Conversion Unit at RAF St Mawgan in Cornwall, and Nos. 120, 201 and 206 Squadrons at RAF Kinloss, Morayshire. The Nimrod MR.2 was the RAF's answer to advances in Soviet submarine technology, which by the late 1970s was beginning to outstrip the search and surveillance systems incorporated in the earlier MR.1.

At the heart of the Nimrod MR.2 is the GEC Avionics AQS 901 accoustic processor. The aircraft carries two independent AQS 901 systems, each able to handle eight sonobuoys. Processed information is presented on cathode-ray tube displays and hard copy recorders. The system, which is based on the GEC Avionics 920 ATC digital computer with a memory capacity of 256K words, has built-in flexibility to handle existing and projected active and passive sonobuoys. One important feature of the AQS 901 is the Computing Devices Fast Fourier Transform (FFT) analyser, which allows the constituent frequencies of a received signal to be separated and averaged over a short period. Regular noise is amplified relative to random noise, even though the latter may be much stronger at a given moment.

Another major equipment item in the Nimrod MR.2 is the Thorn EMI Seachwater radar, replacing the earlier ASV-21 which the Nimrod MR.1 inherited from the Shackleton. Searchwater, which has about fifty times the performance of the ASV-21, is designed to detect and classify small targets against the high clutter caused by heavy seas and bad weather. Narrow beamwidth, pulse compression and frequency agility increase the signal-to-clutter ratio and make the signal difficult to detect and jam.

Digital control of the Searchwater system keeps operator workload down to a manageable level. For example, if only one sector is of interest, the computer decides automatically whether to continue rotation of the antenna and illuminate onto the required sector, or whether to scan backwards and forwards over that sector. The computer varies the detection threshold continuously across the screen to keep false alarm rate down. Once range has been selected, pulse repetition frequency, beamwidth and antenna tilt are controlled by the computer.

Identification Friend or Foe (IFF) is integrated into Searchwater, which has weather and navigation modes as well as search. The system has an extensive track-while-scan capability, but the number of targets which can be tracked individually is classified, as is the system's range and discrimination.

Below: All Nimrods have now been updated to MR2 configuration and fitted with in-flight refuelling probes. Neither Kinloss nor St Mawgan Nimrods carry unit markings. *(Robbie Shaw)*

Opposite: Note the size of the cavernous bomb bay of the Nimrod. This MR2P is also carrying AIM-9 Sidewinder missiles which look rather small when carried on an aircraft of this size. *(Robbie Shaw)*
Overleaf: Despite its age the Buccaneer is still a formidable aircraft. All Buccaneers are now based at Lossiemouth, but the type is always in demand for the airshow circuit. Note the vapour trails as this aircraft demonstrates its ability at the Leuchars airshow. *(Robbie Shaw)*

These systems, together with electronic surveillance measures (ESM) and magnetic anomaly detection (MAD) combine to make the Nimrod MR.2 a very effective anti-submarine warfare aircraft, and the only one — thanks to the AQS 901 — which is capable of handling all sonobuoys in NATO service.

The Nimrod, like all other maritime patrol aircraft, uses three types of sonobuoy to detect, resolve and localise a submarine prior to carrying out an attack. The aircraft first of all sows a pattern of passive omnidirectional buoys to provide overlapping coverage of an area where there is a suspected target; once the latter has been confirmed, passive directional buoys are dropped to resolve it, and it is then pinpointed at the last minute by active directional buoys. The AD sonobuoy used by the Nimrod is the British-designed CAMBS, which provides sufficient data on target bearing, range and Doppler relative speed for the AQS 901 to track the submarine. CAMBS is a command-active buoy, which delays the submarine commander's awareness that he is under attack until the final stage. Having dropped its passive buoys, the Nimrod circles and then begins its attack run along the submarine's anticipated track, updating the target's position by means of passive sonar and then obtaining a last fix by triggering the command-active buoy before the ASW weapons are released.

The principal weapons in the Nimrod's anti-submarine armoury are the air-launched depth charge and the homing torpedo. The depth charge is the British Aerospace Mk. 11 Mod 3, which has a maximum depth of 295 feet (ninety metres) and a 176 lb (80 kg) high-explosive warhead. The aircraft is also cleared to carry the American B57 tactical gravity bomb, an air-dropped nuclear depth bomb whose warhead has a variable yield of between five and ten kilotons and which can operate at a depth of about 3,280 feet (1,000 metres).

The homing torpedo used by the Nimrod is the Marconi Sting Ray, an advanced lightweight 'smart' weapon which functions equally well in both deep and shallow waters. Sting Ray is fitted with an on-board digital computer coupled with a multi-mode multi-beam active/passive sonar and carries an 88 lb (40 kg) shaped

Below: Only just airborne, yet already the landing gear is almost fully retracted as this Buccaneer S2B of 208 Squadron departs Scampton to return to its Lossiemouth base.
*(Robbie Shaw)*

Above: A Buccaneer S2A of the training unit No. 237 OCU.
*(Robbie Shaw)*

charge HE warhead for effective hull penetration. It has a speed of forty-five knots and a range of 6.9 miles (11.1 kilometres). Air dropping trials of Sting Ray were carried out by Nimrods of A&AEE and No. 42 Squadron, which has a specialist torpedo-bomber role within No. 18 Group.

Nimrod is also compatible with anti-ship missiles such as the McDonnell Douglas AGM-84A Harpoon, which has been purchased by the UK MoD to equip the MR.2. This weapon is constantly being upgraded to match the changing threat; the latest version has a very low cruise height, making it difficult to detect and engage by enemy sensors and weapon systems. A solid-fuel Aerojet rocket boosts it to 0.75M in 2.5 seconds, after which it is sustained in cruising flight at 0.85M by a Teledyne CAE J402-CA-400 turbojet for fifteen minutes. The attack phase is controlled by a Texas Instruments PR-53/DSQ-28 two-axis active radar seeker, and the missile carries a 500 lb (225 kg) penetration blast warhead. Maximum range is sixty-eight miles (110 km), which means that carriage of the weapon gives the Nimrod MR.2 a very effective stand-off capability against surface vessels. The AGM-84A is carried in the Nimrod's weapons bay.

The unique air brakes are just opening to enable this Buccaneer S2 to lose speed as it breaks to join the circuit for landing. *(Robbie Shaw)*

For air defence, the Nimrod can carry two AIM-9L Sidewinder AAMs on underwing pylons. This modification was incorporated and cleared for operational use during the Falklands War. Another modification that resulted from that conflict was the addition of a flight refuelling system. AAR is a very important force multiplier for the Nimrod, although operationally it requires very close tactical control between tanker and receiver. The Nimrod MR.2 is an effective system and is likely to remain in service until the end of the century, when it may be replaced by a maritime patrol version of the planned Future International Military Airlifter now under joint study by Britain, France, Federal Germany and the United States. An Outline European Staff Target (OEST) has already been prepared, together with a Mission Need Document that outlines the requirements for replacing Nimrod, the Dassault-Breguet Atlantic, and the Lockheed P-3 Orion in this role.

No. 18 Group's other offensive assets currently comprise Nos. 12 and 208 Squadrons, which operate Buccaneer S.2 aircraft in the anti-shipping strike role from RAF Lossiemouth. Also at Lossiemouth is No. 237 (Buccaneer) OCU. The combined total of available aircraft is around sixty.

The Buccaneer is a very robust aircraft with an excellent low-level performance, having been designed from the outset as a long-range Naval strike and reconnaissance aircraft. Fatigue problems, caused by prolonged low-level operations and diagnosed as a result of accidents in the early 1980s, were overcome by modifications and refurbishment, and the aircraft has enough airframe life to continue in service until at least the mid-1990s.

A Martel missile used by the Buccaneer for attacks against shipping. *(Robbie Shaw)*

In January 1984, under the provisions of Air Staff Target (AST) 1012, thirty-two Buccaneers progressively underwent an extensive mission avionics update to enable them to be armed with up to four British Aerospace Sea Eagle anti-ship missiles per aircraft. Prior to this, the Buccaneer's primary anti-ship missile was the TV-guided Martel, developed by British Aerospace (Hawker Siddeley Dynamics) and the French company Matra; this was to be retained as a backup to Sea Eagle, and the radar-guided version of the missile — whose seeker heads had been disposed of when the Buccaneer was withdrawn from its seaborne role — was also to be re-procured.

Development firings of the British Aerospace Dynamics Sea Eagle began in 1981 and Service evaluation was completed in 1985. A very advanced weapon, Sea Eagle is supplied with target range and bearing data from the aircraft's nav/attack system, together with launch airspeed, wind speed and direction, and other data such as target-selection criteria and ECM information before an attack is initiated. If such information is not available, Sea Eagle may be released on a pre-set heading and left to fly until its own radar seeker detects the target.

After the round has been dropped from the pylon of the launch aircraft the engine air intake cover is jettisoned, allowing the engine — a Microturbo TR1-60 turbojet — to windmill up to speed and start. Under the control of the flight computer, the round descends to sea-skimming level while simultaneously turning on to the target bearing, then begins the flight to the target area. When the flight control computer determines that the missile is nearing the target, radar silence is broken by switching on the J-band pulse-radar seeker. The large scan angle and long range of the seeker ensure that the target will be detected, even if it is fast-moving and taking evasive action. The seeker was designed to cope with the severest weather conditions, and targets having radar cross-sections of 100 m² or more have been detected and tracked from the radar horizon to within a few hundred metres. The performance of the missile, and details of its HE warhead, are classified.

The Sea King HAR3s of 202 Squadron, like other RAF SAR helicopters, are painted a distinctive bright yellow, however aircraft based in the Falklands with 78 Squadron are in an overall grey scheme. As these aircraft are rotated through Finningley for servicing it is inevitable that occasionally they will serve in the UK. At the time of this photograph 202 Squadron 'B' Flight at Brawdy had an aircraft in each scheme on strength.
*(Robbie Shaw)*

The role of the two Buccaneer S.2A/B squadrons which are equipped with Sea Eagle is to cover the Iceland-Faeroes-United Kingdom Gap, through which Soviet task forces would attempt to break out into the North Atlantic, and to deter amphibious landings on the north-west coast of Norway. In the latter case, Sea Eagle, with its longer range, would be used to attack escort ships, leaving Martel-equipped Buccaneers to strike at softer targets such as landing ships. For attacks on static targets, including port installations, the Buccaneer is equipped with the Pave Spike/Paveway laser-guided bomb system. For overwater operations the aircraft has the Ferranti Blue Parrot radar — much updated over the years — an inertial navigation system and a head-up display.

The Buccaneer carries the Westinghouse ALQ-101-10 ECM pod, but can also be fitted with the Sky Shadow, developed for the Tornado IDS. Other defensive equipment includes two internally-mounted Tracor AN/ALE-40 chaff/flare dispensers, which can eject sequences of up to thirty chaff clusters and fifteen infra-red decoy flares per unit.

Buccaneers have the ability to refuel one another under the 'buddy-buddy' system, as well as refuelling from the tanker force, and this is a valuable extra asset in terms of rapid deployment. From forward airfields in Norway, the Buccaneer has sufficient combat radius to strike hard, in most weathers, against Soviet installations on the Murmansk Peninsula. For self-defence the aircraft can carry two AIM-9L Sidewinders. In war, part of the Buccaneer Force would probably operate in the 'Wild Weasel' defence suppression role. When the aircraft reach the limit of their airframe life in the 1990s, they will almost certainly be replaced by Tornados.

The operations of No. 18 Group's offensive forces must always be seen in the context of wider NATO operations. Nimrods would operate in concert with other NATO maritime patrol aircraft, Buccaneers alongside USAF F-111 strike aircraft assigned to the Northern Front. Given the present downward trend of Allied maritime force levels and the unprecedented rise in those of the Warsaw Pact, NATO is seeking to structure its conventional maritime force and improve its ability to conduct sustained operations; if it fails to do so, NATO will be at risk in the Atlantic.

Across the board, SACLANT is still about forty per cent short of requirements, including maritime patrol and strike aircraft. These forces are required for carrying out the basic principles of NATO maritime strategy, which are: to contain the enemy before he gets clear of his base areas; to establish layers of forces or systems as far forward as possible; and to maintain the initiative and exploit

Below: The sight every downed airman wants to see — a yellow helicopter! The crewman is being lowered on the winch during this practice. *(Robbie Shaw)*

Opposite: Although established for rescuing downed aircrew, the vast majority of those rescued by the RAF rescue services are civilians. In this instance, ably assisted by the local coastguard, a Sea King rescues a civilian cut off by the tide at the base of a steep cliff. *(Robbie Shaw*

strategic and tactical advantage whenever they occur. If, in a conflict, the Soviet Northern Fleet is not contained north of the Greenland-Iceland-UK Gap, then the battle for the Atlantic and ultimately the defence of Western Europe would become critical. There is every need to underline the fact that No. 18 Group has an enormous responsibility; in time of war, safeguarding its slender resources would have to receive the highest priority.

The Soviet Naval Command is well aware of NATO's strategy in northern waters, and in recent years has carried out large-scale exercises to simulate NATO containment operations. One of the largest was held in the summer of 1985, when at least fifty surface vessels, including some of the USSR's newest warships, supported by a substantial force of submarines and maritime aircraft, simulated a two-pronged attempt by NATO forces to block off the Northern Fleet rounding the North Cape from their Murmansk bases. In this exercise, the Russians set up two submarine barriers, plus a third barrier of surface vessels, submarines and ASW aircraft, across the Norwegian Sea and the Greenland-Iceland-UK Gap.

## Search and Rescue

The United Kingdom is divided into two Search and Rescue Regions, with Rescue Co-ordination Centres at Pitreavie Castle, near Edinburgh, and Mount Wise, Plymouth. No. 18 Group has two helicopter squadrons dedicated to the SAR task; Nos. 22 and 202 Squadrons,

Although lacking the range and capabilities of the Sea King, the Wessex HC2 still plays a vital role in the Search and Rescue network. It is likely that further Sea Kings will be ordered to replace the Wessex of 22 Squadron. *(Robbie Shaw)*

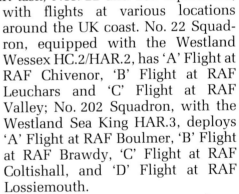

with flights at various locations around the UK coast. No. 22 Squadron, equipped with the Westland Wessex HC.2/HAR.2, has 'A' Flight at RAF Chivenor, 'B' Flight at RAF Leuchars and 'C' Flight at RAF Valley; No. 202 Squadron, with the Westland Sea King HAR.3, deploys 'A' Flight at RAF Boulmer, 'B' Flight at RAF Brawdy, 'C' Flight at RAF Coltishall, and 'D' Flight at RAF Lossiemouth.

No. 18 Group's SAR Squadrons share the search and rescue task with the Royal Navy and, as required, with the USAF's 67th Aerospace Rescue and Recovery Squadron, which is based at RAF Woodbridge and operates HH-53C helicopters under the control of USAFE.

RAF SAR helicopters are deployed in flights of two aircraft. Their record in peacetime operations has been excellent, but in a war situation it is questionable whether enough aircraft would be available to carry out this demanding task adequately. It should be recalled that the RAF no longer has any marine craft units for close-in rescue work; these disbanded in 1986. Moreover, RAF and RN SAR helicopters — unlike their USAF/USN counterparts — have no combat capability, which under certain operational conditions could be a disadvantage.

# CHAPTER FOUR
## RAF Support Command

With its Headquarters at RAF Brampton, near Huntingdon, RAF Support Command came into being in its present form in June 1977 following the merger of the former Support Command and Training Command. Its responsibilities are enormous, ranging from flying training to the provision of medical facilities throughout the RAF.

The training aim, broadly, is to maintain the supply of officers and men with the professional qualities on which the standards of the Royal Air Force depend. The range of training tasks covers the selection and initial general service training of all officers; aircrew training; specialist training for officers in ground branches; basic, trade training, further and post-graduate training for airmen and airwomen; apprentice training; the training of flying instructors; air and ground training for personnel and Commonwealth and foreign air forces and for other government departments; and refresher flying training for officers transferring from ground to flying appointments.

Support Command administers, via UAS HQ at RAF Cranwell, sixteen University Air Squadrons equipped with Bulldog T.1 basic trainers. The UASs are affiliated to fifty-five universities, colleges and polytechnics throughout the UK. The majority of UAS students are signed up as members of the RAF Volunteer Reserve (RAFVR); about thirty per cent are being sponsored through University by a Royal Air Force cadetship. They are commissioned with the rank of Acting Pilot Officer (APO), receive an APO's salary, and are committed to serve in the RAF for sixteen years or up to the age of thirty-eight, whichever comes latest. The remainder are Cadet Pilots (CPs) and are not required to make a similar commitment.

The squadrons are far from glorified recruiting agencies; about thirty-three per cent of those entering pilot training with the RAF are ex-UAS, and the ratio is even higher — around forty-seven per cent — among those who successfully complete their pilot training and go into productive service. With the cost of training a pilot to fast-jet standard about £1.7 million, any system which can guarantee this level of success is a wise investment.

Having successfully passed through the Officer and Aircrew Selection Centre (OASC) at RAF Biggin Hill, a candidate for aircrew training — like all other officer cadets — must undergo an eighteen-week Initial Officer Training (IOT) course at RAF

Below: Over forty years old and still going strong, the Chipmunk is likely to remain in RAF service into the twenty-first century. This Chipmunk T10 of the Elementary Flying Training Squadron (EFTS) still bears the insignia of its previous title — the Flying Selection Squadron (FSS). *(Robbie Shaw)*

Above: First deliveries of the Tucano T1 were to the Central Flying School (CFS) at Scampton, with 7 FTS at Church Fenton equipping in 1989. This CFS aircraft was photographed at its Scampton base. *(Robbie Shaw)*
Opposite: A Bulldog T1 of London University Air Squadron over the Oxfordshire countryside near its base at Abingdon. *(Robbie Shaw)*

Cranwell. He then goes on to the RAF Aeromedical Training Centre at RAF North Luffenham, where he is issued with flying clothing, taught various survival drills — including the management of oxygen systems — and decompressed. The next step, unless he has undergone a minimum of thirty hours flying experience in a course recognised by the RAF (which includes previous training with a UAS or successful completion of an Air Cadets Flying Scholarship), is to undergo a flying assessment at the Flying Selection Squadron, RAF Swinderby.

The FSS, which was set up in 1974, operates Chipmunk T.10 trainers and its primary function is to eliminate, at this early and relatively inexpensive stage, those candidates who have no flying aptitude or who are incompatible with flying because of some other factor, such as chronic and constant air-sickness. The FSS course lasts six weeks and involves some fifteen hours flying; about seventy-five per cent of the candidates make the grade. Some of those who fail decide to leave the Service, but many apply for training as navigators or AEOs or transfer to a non-flying branch.

Basic flying training, involving a thirty-seven-week course and ninety-three flying hours, is carried out at No. 1 Flying Training School, RAF Linton-on-Ouse, No. 7 FTS at RAF Church Fenton, and the Royal Air Force College, Cranwell. In the latter case, UAS graduates who have gained their Preliminary Flying Badge undergo a short course lasting thirty-one weeks, with seventy-five hours flying. On completion of the first phase of their basic flying course students are split into three streams: fast jet, multi-engine and helicopter. Up to this point, students have trained on the British Aerospace Jet Provost T.Mk. 3A; students selected for the fast jet stream go on to complete a further fifteen weeks and fifty-seven flying hours on the Jet Provost T.Mk. 5A.

After giving many years of sterling service to the RAF — the first mark was delivered to the Flying Training Schools in 1955 — the Jet Provost is now being replaced by the Shorts Tucano T.1. Designed by Embraer of Brazil, the Tucano was selected as the RAF's future basic trainer in the face of stiff competition from the

Below: The excellent Hawk is used by 4 FTS at Valley in the advanced training role. This aircraft wears a small CFS badge forward of the intake, as it had been on loan to the Red Arrows during the winter season whilst their own aircraft were on maintenance. *(Robbie Shaw)*

Swiss-designed Pilatus PC-9, and 130 aircraft are being built under licence by Shorts of Belfast. Powered by a 1,100 shp Garrett TPE331-12B turboprop, the Tucano has a tandem cockpit layout, an advantage for students in the fast jet stream who progress to the Hawk T.1; the fact that it is turboprop-powered also provides valuable experience in this type of engine for students in the multi-engine stream. Aircraft for the RAF are structurally strengthened, and have a design fatigue life of 12,000 hours. The first examples were delivered to CFS at RAF Scampton in June 1988, and the initial Tucano course formed with No. 1 FTS at RAF Linton-on-Ouse in 1989.

There is no doubt that the Tucano will make the transition to the Hawk a good deal easier for students that was the case with the Jet Provost, with its side-by-side seating. Advanced flying on the Hawk T.1 is carried out at RAF Valley, Anglesey, with No. 4 FTS; the first Hawks were delivered there in November 1976, replacing the Hawker Siddeley Gnat T.1. Today, No. 4 FTS is the RAF's only advanced flying training school. Fast-jet students spend twenty-two weeks at Valley, completing a further seventy-five hours flying, and are then awarded their pilot's brevet before going on to one of the Hawk-equipped Tactical Weapons Units described in chapter one.

Above: The ageing Jet Provost T3A is now being replaced by the Shorts Tucano. This aircraft of No. 1 FTS at Linton-on-Ouse has special tail markings to signify it is the mount of the Support Command Jet Provost display pilot for 1989, Flying Officer Andy Offer. *(Robbie Shaw)*

Students in the multi-engine stream complete a further twenty-seven hours in Jet Provosts (or Tucanos, in the future training system) before beginning their course with the Multi-Engine Training School at RAF Finningley, flying Jetstream T.1 aircraft. The Jetstream is powered by two Astazou turboprops and eleven are in RAF service. The original RAF order was for twenty-six aircraft, but some of these were delivered to the Royal Navy under the designation Jetstream T.2.

Navigator, Air Electronics Officer and Air Engineer training is also undertaken at RAF Finningley in the Jet Provosts and Dominie T.1s of No. 6 FTS. The Jet Provosts are used to provide low-level navigation training for future fast-jet navigators. The Dominie, twenty of which are in RAF service, is the military version of the British Aerospace (Hawker Siddeley) 125 executive jet; it replaced the Vickers Varsity in the training role and carries three navigators, two students and an instructor. The navigation course lasts fourteen months; the Air Engineers and Air Electronics Officers' courses last about a year.

Helicopter training is carried out at Shawbury, where No. 2 FTS is equipped with the Gazelle HT.3 and Wessex HT.2. The Gazelle course lasts eighteen weeks and involves about eighty-fours flying; students then graduate to the Wessex, logging a further fifty-four hours in three months.

Although much younger than the T3A, the Jet Provost T5A is also being replaced by the Tucaco. This trio of 1 FTS aircraft were photographed on a landaway exercise at Brawdy.
*(Robbie Shaw)*

## The Central Flying School

The Central Flying School (CFS), which has its Headquarters at RAF Scampton, comprises fixed-wing and helicopter elements which undertake the training of all flying instructors in the Royal Air Force, Royal Navy and Army Air Corps, besides training instructors for other air forces. The CFS also houses an inspectorate, known as the Examining Wing, whose duty is the quality control of flying training throughout the Command, and indeed throughout the Service. The Central Flying School is also the parent unit of the Royal Air Force Aerobatic Team, the Red Arrows.

## Headquarters Air Cadets

HQ Air Cadets, at RAF Newton, has a Group status within Support Command. It is functionally controlled by MoD. There are over 1,000 local squadrons of the Air Training Corps in the United Kingdom, together with many Royal Air Force Sections of the Combined Cadet Force, administered through several Regional HQs and run by officers of the Royal Air Force Volunteer Reserve (Training Branch), assisted by civilian instructors and — in the case of the ATC — some Warrant Officers. To provide cadets with first-hand flying experience, HQAC maintains thirteen Air Experience Flights (AEF); and twenty-seven Gliding Schools. The AEFs are equipped with the Chipmunk T.10 and the Gliding Schools use a range of equipment that includes self-launching gliders. The value of the Air Cadet organisation to the Royal Air Force as a whole can not be over-emphasized; it provides young men and women with a valuable insight into Service life which stands them in good stead if they decide to join, and encourages qualities of character and leadership which are useful in any walk of life.

## Headquarters Command and Staff Training

Based at Bracknell, this HQ is responsible for the RAF Staff College and is functionally controlled by MoD, but administratively controlled by HQ Support Command.

Top left: The Dominie T1 is used on the basic navigation course at Finningley, which often includes airways training trips to the continent at weekends, usually to RAF Germany bases. Photographed transiting through Bruggen on a Friday evening are five Dominies of 6 FTS. *(Robbie Shaw)*
Bottom left: The Bulldog is used by the CFS to train instructors for the University Air squadrons. *(Robbie Shaw)*
Opposite: The Multi-Engined Training Squadron (METS), a component of 6 FTS at Finningley, used the twin-engined Scottish Aviation Jetstream T1. *(Robbie Shaw)*

### Airman Training

The distinctive feature about the training of 'ground airmen' in the RAF is that, with the exception of men destined for the RAF Regiment, the object is not so much to make the trainees fit to fight but to enable them to give impeccable support to the relatively small number of officers and men who would be directly involved in operations. There is nevertheless plenty of challenge, variety and interest both in the training itself and in the range of tasks to which it is directed. Airmen must have expert knowledge of complex aircraft, advanced electrical and electronic systems, modern instrumentation, automatic test equipment, radio and radar, propulsion units, weapon systems, specialist and general-pupose ground vehicles, photographic apparatus — in short, a multitude of equipments ranging from the elementary to the upper reaches of refined technology. Outside the engineering and maintenance fields, men must be trained as air traffic controllers, air defence operators, medical and dental assistants, computer operators, communications specialists and for many other tasks which have to be performed consistently well to enable the Royal Air Force to operate with economy and safety in peace, and with immediate efficiency in war.

Recruits enter as adults in most trades from the age of sixteen-and-a-half and as technician apprentices at the same age in the aircraft and electronic trades. Airmen are given their basic training at RAF Swinderby and airwomen (see WRAF section) at RAF Hereford. The RAF Apprentice Schools are RAF Halton, RAF Locking, RAF Cosford and RAF St Athan.

### The Communications Task

Support Command is, through its Signals Headquarters at North Luffenham, responsible for operating the elements of the Defence Communication Network which are provided and manned by the RAF. Operation is subject to the day-to-day functional control of the DCN. In this field of strategic communications the Command is the sole system and engineering design authority in the DCN worldwide. It also acts as a consultant to MoD, other RAF

Below and opposite: The Central Flying School at Scampton trains Qualified Flying Instructors (QFIs) on both the Jet Provost T3A and T5A. *(Robbie Shaw)*

Above: A few Hawk T1s are also kept on the strength of the CFS at Scampton, and both these and the 4 FTS machines adopted a new colour scheme in 1989, in which the upper surfaces are painted dark blue. *(Robbie Shaw)*

Commands, and to Commonwealth and Allied Air Forces on all aspects of communications.

The operating resonsibilities divide into four categories. First there is a large complex of HF transmitter and receiver facilities in the UK, including communications centres with automatic message routing equipment; operations include those on behalf of Strike Command, the Military Air Traffic Organisation, NATO, and the Meteorological Office. The second category is message relay centres, some manual, some automatic. The third category comprises the main operations of the Skynet satellite communications system, the UK control centre for which is at Oakhanger. The fourth category comprises the rationalised Army/RAF Telegraph Automatic Switching System (TASS) in the UK, the special network dealing solely with aircraft movements known as the RAF Airmove Network (RAFAN), and the normal administrative telephone network.

The Command also provides aerial erection service on a worldwide basis, embracing the fields of communications, radars and navigation aids. The men required for this highly specialised work are trained by the Command at the Aerial Erectors School, Digby.

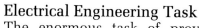

### Electrical Engineering Task

The enormous task of providing ground radio engineering services for the whole of the RAF, at home and overseas, is the responsibility of No. 90 (Signals) Group, which is now part of Support Command. These responsibilities range over the entire field of communications equipment, air traffic control and defence radar systems, ground based navigational aids, and electronic warfare. They comprise design, manufacture, selection and survey of sites, installation, commissioning, including flight checking and calibration, and above all, planning and management of the complete tasks.

After commissioning an installation, the Command usually remains responsible for assisting the operational units to maintain it in use. This involves regular flight performance checking of radars, navigation and approach aids using aircraft of Strike Command, and the completion of major routine servicing and repairs by the Ground Radio Servicing Centre. The Command's services provide the engineering support for the RAF's contribution to the Defence Communication Network throughout the world. It has special responsibilities for installation, design and overall installation management for all Skynet satellite communications system earth stations.

Above: Shawbury is home to Support Command's helicopter training fleet. The Gazelle HT3 is used by both 2 FTS and the CFS Helicopter Squadron. *(Robbie Shaw)*
Opposite: Successful completion of the Gazelle course will see the student progress to the larger, twin-engined Wessex HC2. *(Robbie Shaw)*

To discharge the design responsibilities there is at Medmenham a large engineering design staff of chartered and technician engineers, technicians and draughtsmen. Manufacturing resources include a precision engineering factory at Woolwich and a general mechanical and engineering capability at the Signals Engineering Establishment, RAF Henlow.

No. 30 Maintenance Unit, at RAF Sealand, is the main airborne electronic, electrical and instrument engineering unit. Large workshops and test facilities are laid out on production lines to enable the unit to produce over 100,000 items per year. No. 30 MU, which is part Service and part civilian manned, provides a direct exchange and loan repair scheme for avionic equipment in use in the RAF. The unit operates its own road service to units in the UK and Germany, and exchanges serviceable for unserviceable equipment on a one-for-one basis with a minimum amount of paperwork. The direct exchange scheme for electronic, electrical and instrument equipment saves a great deal of money. Initial buys of equipment need smaller repair 'floats', and flying units do not need to be provided with the high expensive test equipment which they would otherwise need to service the equipment to the same depth, and the numbers of highly skilled tradesmen needed at operational units can be kept to a minimum. The service is also provided to a number of RN, Army and MoD Research stations in the UK and, by air, for units overseas.

## Aircraft Engineering Task

Support Command's largest contribution, in manpower and capital resources, is devoted to engineering in support of the Royal Air Force, and for the fixed-wing aircraft of the Royal Navy and the Army Air Corps. The principal engineering tasks concern aircraft, and scheduled major servicing, rectification, reconditioning and modification of aircraft are undertaken at two main centres, RAF

Top left: Headquarters Air Cadets uses both tow launched and powered gliders to give air experience to the Air Cadet Squadrons. The obsolete Cadet and Sedberghs were replaced a few years ago by the Grob 103 which they have named Viking. *(Robbie Shaw)*

Bottom left: The Venture T2 equips gliding schools throughout the country, but is currently in the process of being replaced by the Grob 109. This Venture of 612 Gliding School was photographed over Oxfordshire near its base at Benson. *(Robbie Shaw)*

Opposite: A well known component of the CFS is the RAF's aerobatic team, the Red Arrows. *(Robbie Shaw)*

Abingdon in Oxfordshire and RAF St Athan in Wales. These units also hold stocks of fixed-wing aircraft, which they prepare for storage and maintain against deterioration.

The engineering unit at RAF St Athan has an Aircraft Servicing Wing and a General Engineering Wing. The former is responsible for major servicing of the Tornado, Victor K.2, Buccaneer S.2 and Phantom, while the General Engineering Wing carries out major servicing of engines for the Hawk, Jaguar and Tornado. RAF Abingdon's Aircraft Servicing Wing carries out major servicing of Hawk and Jaguar aircraft. In addition, Abingdon houses the Repair and Salvage Squadron, which is responsible for the salvage and repair of crashed RAF, Army and RN aircraft around the world. The Squadron has a Battle Damage Repair Flight, whose task is to make good battle damage by various means so that aircraft can be returned to service as quickly as possible. The RSS also sends teams of tradesmen to RAF stations to undertaken aircraft modifications and repairs which are beyond the capability of unit personnel but which do not necessitate the aircraft being returned to a Support Command unit.

In addition to the major aircraft engineering tasks, Support Command repairs almost any kind of equipment when it is expedient and economical to do so — parachutes, ground equipment, furniture and domestic equipment, for example.

Below and opposite: Fire crews regularly practise with 'hot' fires. *(Robbie Shaw)*

## Supply Task

The supply task of Support Command is twofold: first, to provide a complete functional supply service for the Royal Air Force at home and abroad, and also air stores and accommodation stores for the Royal Navy and Army; and second, to provide supply support for the Command's many and varied engineering commitments. The size and composition of the Command's supply units vary according to their respective functions, from large Equipment Supply Depots to comparatively small Petroleum Supply Depots.

The Equipment Supply Depots hold about one million different types of technical and domestic equipment. Quantities vary from a few months' to several years' consumption, according to whether the item can be quickly replenished or can be bought in economic quantity only when the manufacturer is tooled up to produce it. The number of different items held in stock is far greater, and the variety wider, than would be found in any one civilian firm in the UK. The stocks are at present distributed among major depots at RAF Stafford, RAF Carlisle and RAF Quedgeley.

Over the years the techniques of stock recording and stock location, and the speedy handling of items of equipment, have been continually improved. Today, the highest priority demands for equipment are fully processed within six hours of their receipt at a depot, and the lowest priority within seven days. This service operates twenty-four hours a day, all year round. The Automatic Data Processing Computer at the Supply Control Centre, RAF Stanbridge, holds central records of every item of spare equipment held throughout the Royal Air Force; the Equipment Supply Depots and all RAF stations at home and overseas are connected to the computer and daily-corrected records are maintained. As a result, the computer is able to direct that any urgently required item of equipment is either to be despatched from the appropriate depot or, if quicker, to be transferred from another RAF station.

The equipment is housed in large storage sheds, mostly on dispersed sites spread over a wide area. The internal road network at Stafford, for example, covers some twenty miles. Stocks are grouped

according to handling characteristics and frequency of issue; for example, all small items are allocated to high density, easily accessible storage irrespective of range. The depot computers, capable of processing up to 2,000 orders at a time in location sequence, ensure that a high degree of productivity is maintained.

RAF Quedgeley, in Gloucestershire, is used exclusively for the storage and supply of accommodation stores for all three services; all technical items of equipment are concentrated at RAF Stafford and RAF Carlisle. Other units include RAF Cardington, which produces, stores and distributes to the RAF, the other Services and Government Departments most of their daily requirements of compressed gases; RAF Chilmark, where the Ammunition Supply Depot (ASD) is responsible for the day-to-day supply of explosives, oil and lubricants to the RAF worldwide; and twenty-two Petroleum Supply Depots, dispersed throughout the UK, which hold bulk supplies of aviation fuels for day-to-day and emergency use. The PSDs are operated under contract by civilian oil companies.

## Administrative Task

The administrative task is to provide support of a satisfactory standard for a minimum cost to those units not under functional control but for which the Command has been made responsible. This is a diverse list including the Personnel Management Centre at Gloucester, the RAF elements of the Procurement Executive at Farnborough, Boscombe Down, Bedford and Pershore, the Institute of Aviation Medicine, Careers Information Offices, and Bands. In all, Support Command has varying degrees of administrative responsibility for some 180 units located throughout the United Kingdom, together with some overseas units.

## Medical Task

The medical task is to examine and, where appropriate, treat personnel needing medical attention beyond that available at normal Service stations. To attain this aim Support Command controls the RAF hospitals at Ely, Halton and Wroughton. It also controls the Joint Service Medical Rehabilitation Unit at Chessington, and the RAF Medical Rehabilitation Unit at Headley Court. The task of these units, as their name suggests, is to restore to the best possible standard of fitness those patients recovering from some form or degree of incapacity. The Command also controls the Central Medical Establishment, which provides a centralised consultancy service for RAF and other personnel, as well as normal medical facilities for Service personnel working in the Air Force Department of the Ministry of Defence. The Command is also responsible for the Institute of Pathology and Tropical Medicine at Halton and the RAF Chest Unit at Midhurst. RAF hospitals and other medical establishments are staffed by male and female personnel of the Princess Mary's Royal Air Force Nursing Service.

# CHAPTER FIVE
## The Royal Air Force Regiment

T he Royal Air Force Regiment is responsible for the protection of RAF airfields and other installations against both ground and low-level air attack, for the training of RAF personnel in ground defence and for the provision of advisers in a number of specialist fields. It also provides the RAF's crash-rescue and fire services in conjunction with the Air Force Department Fire Service. The Regiment is unique in that it is constituted as a Corps within the Royal Air Force, having been formed by Royal Warrant of King George VI in February, 1942. Her Majesty the Queen is Air Commodore-in-Chief of the Regiment.

With its HQ at RAF Catterick, in North Yorkshire, the Regiment is organised into a number of mobile field and low-level air defence squadrons (LLAD), with small tactical Wing Headquarters to co-ordinate the operations of two or more such units. The primary low-level air defence weapon is the British Aerospace Rapier missile, and the role of the RAF Regiment units operating it as part of the UK air defence system is described in chapter two.

In addition, the UK-based element of the RAF Regiment has four light armoured squadrons: Nos. 51 and 58 (No. 3 Wing) at RAF Catterick and Nos. 15 and 2 (Para) which form No. 5 Wing at RAF Hullavington. No. 2 (Para) Squadron is a specialist unit and exists for rapid overseas deployment in the event of a threat situation arising in any part of the world where the UK Government has defence responsibilities; its task would be to secure and defend landing facilities for elements of the Hercules Transport Force flying in reinforcements.

Senior Aircraftsman Jay Taylor of the Queen's Colour Squadron, which although primarily a ceremonial unit, remains proficient in all the aspects of warfare required of it.
*(Robbie Shaw)*

Principal equipment of the light armoured squadrons is the FV101 Scorpion light tank and the FV103 Spartan armoured personnel carrier; each squadron has six Scorpions and fifteen Spartans. The Scorpion is fitted with a 76 mm gun, the L23A1, which fires HE, armour-piercing and smoke ammunition over a range of about 2,200 metres. The tank is also equipped with a laser rangefinder. The main function of the Scorpion is to engage armoured personnel carriers and reconnaissance vehicles, but it can also engage infantry using Canister ammunition. The Spartan APC, which carries up to five fully-equipped men, is fitted with a 7.62 mm L37A1 machine-gun and two four-barrel smoke dischargers.

In addition to the above equipment, each light armoured squadron has one FV105 Sultan command vehicle, which can carry up to six men of the Squadron HQ staff. Armament is one 7.62 mm L7A2 General Purpose Machine Gun, and like the Spartan this vehicle is fitted with two four-barrel smoke dischargers. Finally, each light armoured squadron has one FV106 Samson armoured recovery vehicle, which carries a similar armament to the Sultan.

A light armoured squadron has a strength of about 150 men. In time of threat, the relatively few squadrons on the Order of Battle would be reinforced by units of the Territorial Army and Home Defence Forces, giving a substantial increase in manpower. The threat is now recognised, primarily, as groups of highly-trained SPETZNAZ (Soviet Special Forces), backed up by locally recruited subversive groups drawn from various terrorist organisations, one of whose main targets would be the Rapier low-level air defence systems deployed some distance out from the perimeters of key airfields. To help meet this threat — which must not be under-estimated — several Royal Auxiliary Air Force Regiment Squadrons have been formed on a territorial basis; these are No. 2503 Squadron at RAF Scampton, No. 2620 Squadron at RAF Marham, No. 2622 Squadron at RAF Lossiemouth, No. 2623 Squadron at RAF Honington, No. 2624 Squadron at RAF Brize Norton, and No. 2625 Squadron at RAF St Mawgan. These squadrons are equipped with Land Rovers for airfield perimeter patrol duties, and personnel are armed with automatic weapons.

One other Royal Auxiliary Air Force Regiment unit, No. 2729 Squadron, is deployed at RAF Waddington on air defence duties and is equipped with an Oerlikon/Fledermaus AAA system captured from the Argentinian Army during the Falklands War.

Details of RAF Regiment units supporting the RAF in Germany will be found in the appropriate section.

A Rapier launcher which comprises of four missiles. These are deployed close to the perimeter of airfields to defend against air attack. *(Robbie Shaw)*

# CHAPTER SIX
## The Women's Royal Air Force

The Women's Royal Air Force came into being on 1 April 1918, concurrent with the formation of the Royal Air Force. Between then and 1920, when it was disbanded, 32,000 women served in its ranks.

In 1938, the impending threat of war resulted in the Imperial Defence Committee changing its mind over the policy of not recruiting women for the Services in peacetime, and on 9 September the signing of a Royal Warrant brought the Auxiliary Territorial Service (ATS) into existence. By 28 June, 1939, the forty-eight RAF Companies of the ATS transferred to form the nucleus of the new Women's Auxiliary Air Force. A few days later, wearing their new blue uniforms for the first time, members of the WAAF took part in the national defence rally held in Hyde Park, where the salute was taken by HM King George VI.

Then numbering less than 2,000 women in one officer branch and six trades, the Service expanded until, by mid-1943, nearly 182,000 women were serving in twenty-two officer branches and seventy-five trades. These women were an integral part of the Royal Air Force, and served both at home and overseas. Many were decorated for gallantry and outstanding service, and hundreds were mentioned in despatches. In 1946, Parliament announced that it was planned to retain women in the Armed Forces of the Crown on a permanent basis, and as a result of this the Women's Royal Air Force was re-formed on 1 February 1949. Members of the WAAF were given the choice of completing their service in the WAAF or transferring to the regular force. All new entrants were commissioned or enlisted in the Royal Air Force, and the only restriction placed on their employment was that they should not undertake combatant duties.

Women continued to do their officer or recruit training in a primarily female environment, but their professional training was undertaken with their male colleagues. On completion of this they were employed in RAF posts on stations having suitable accommodation for women, and the only posts specifically established for them were those dealing with the administration of women in the Royal Air Force. At higher levels these included a senior officer at Group and Command HQ, an Inspector of the WRAF on the staff of the Inspector General of the RAF and officers on the staff of Director WRAF, itself established as an Air Commodore post.

Things began to change radically in the early 1950s, when the first women attended the RAF Staff College course. Later in that decade it was decided that women should carry out their officer training with the RAF, and in 1961 the WRAF officer cadet unit was disbanded. In 1959 the trade of Air Quartermaster was opened to women; in 1962 this trade was awarded aircrew status and ten airwomen were among members of the first course to qualify for the flying brevet. On 1 October 1970, Air Quartermasters were re-named Air Loadmasters, a title that more accurately reflected their duties.

The first women to be trained as Air Traffic Controllers took up their duties in the early 1960s, some of them having had previous experience as Fighter Controllers. The post of Inspector WRAF was abolished in 1968, and in the same year the rank titles of women officers were brought into line with their male counterparts. In 1970, with the introduction of the Graduate Entry Scheme, the first women were accepted as students at the RAF College, Cranwell. During the same year, with the introduction of the military salary, airwomen over the age of twenty could elect to live out of camp subject to the exigencies of the Service and suitable civilian accommodation being available. Since 1971, married airwomen have been able to serve on units with their husbands even if there are no other women members of the Service on the station. In 1971, the first woman to gain promotion to air rank in open competition with her RAF colleagues was promoted to Air Commodore.

Although the RAF has only recently accepted women for training as pilots and navigators, the WRAF have been employed in most career structures for many years, including air traffic control.
*(Robbie Shaw)*

Today, women members of the Royal Air Force are employed in fifteen of the twenty RAF trade groups and in all the officer branches with the exception of the RAF Regiment. They perform a vital and indispensable task within the Service, filling a great many key positions ranging from Fighter Control to the important Intelligence function of Radio Operator (Voice).

Until 1989, the only RAF aircrew category in which women were allowed to serve was that of Air Loadmaster, but female personnel are now being encouraged to apply for flying training as pilots and navigators. They will not fly combat aircraft; instead, they will be confined to transports, tankers, AEW aircraft and search and rescue helicopters. Some female fighter controllers are also being trained to operate on board the Sentry AEW.1 AWACS aircraft.

# CHAPTER SEVEN
## RAF Germany — The Threat

L ike all other Royal Air Force formations assigned or earmarked for
assignment to NATO, RAF Germany combines certain national
tasks with its NATO role. It is, however, probably more closely
integrated into the structure of NATO's Allied Command Europe
(ACE) than any other part of the Royal Air Force.

Its national commitment is defined as:

> 'In peacetime, under responsibilities retained by the United
> Kingdom pending the conclusion of a German peace treaty, and
> in close integration with NATO, the defence of the integrity of
> the air space of the northern half of the Federal Republic of
> Germany and, with the United States Air Force and the French
> Air Force, the maintenance of access to Berlin in the three air
> corridors.'

By far the greater proportion of RAF Germany's effort, however,
goes into fulfilling its other main task — the provision of conventional
and nuclear strike/attack, reconnaissance and air defence forces for
the immediate support of any NATO land operations (or, in
peacetime, exercises) as part of the NATO Second Allied Tactical Air
Force (2 ATAF). It is in this second role that RAF Germany is
responsible for maintaining Britain's main air contribution to the
defence of the European mainland.

Although in peacetime RAF Germany is a completely autonomous
Command of the Royal Air Force, responsible through its RAF
Commander-in-Chief direct to the UK Ministry of Defence, its
squadrons train and exercise continuously as part of 2 ATAF. This
formation, which in peacetime consists of a headquarters staff only, is
the NATO formation which would carry out offensive and defensive
air operations over Northern Germany, Belgium and Holland in the
event of war. Its area of responsibility covers an immense 60,000
square miles, bounded by a line running along the borders of the
Federal Republic in the east to the Danish border in the north, out
over the North Sea, south along the Franco-Belgian border to the
northern tip of Luxembourg, and then north-east in a straight line
across central Germany to Kassel and Gottingen on the border with
the German Democratic Republic.

To defend this area, 2 ATAF would have under its command in
wartime fighter aircraft for defensive operations against a hostile air
threat, fighter-bomber squadrons to give close support to NATO land
forces, reconnaissance squadrons tasked to provide rapid intelligence
information for army and air commanders, and bomber squadrons to

interdict enemy targets — these squadrons having both conventional and nuclear capability. These forces are provided by squadrons from four separate air forces: the Luftwaffengruppe Nord of the German Air Force, Royal Air Force Germany, the Royal Netherlands Air Force and the Belgian Air Force.

South of 2 ATAF's area of responsibility lies the area of a similar formation, the Fourth Allied Tactical Air Force (4 ATAF), which comprises squadrons from the German, American and Canadian air forces. Together, these two Allied Tactical Air Forces form the air element of Allied Forces Central Europe, and through this higher-level formation are available to the Supreme Allied Commander Europe, under whose command they would come in time of war.

The air threat that faces 2 and 4 ATAF is formidable. Deployed in the GDR, the Soviet Air Force's 16th Air Army musters about 1,000 combat aircraft, together with around 200 transports and helicopters; this formation supports the Group of Soviet Forces in Germany (GSFG) which would be the spearhead of any attack on NATO's Central Front. The principal ground-attack type is the MiG-27 Flogger variable geometry aircraft, which in addition to a wide range of external offensive stores has a build-in 23 mm Gatling-type gun; the MiG-23 is a multi-role version with a limited look-down capability, thanks to a High Lark radar and an infra-red sensor under the nose.

A major threat is also presented by the MiG-25 Foxbat and MiG-31 Foxhound. The latest Foxbat version is the Foxbat-E, which is a dedicated defence suppression aircraft armed with AS-11 anti-radiation missiles; the MiG-31, a developed version, has true look-down/shootdown capability and improved low-level performance. Two dedicated air-superiority fighters, the MiG-29 Fulcrum and the Sukhoi Su-27 Flanker, are also operational with Soviet units in the GDR; the Fulcrum, which is in the F-16/F-18 class, has a pulse-Doppler radar and carries up to six AA-10 medium-range AAMs, as well as a six-barrel 30 mm gun, while the Flanker, which is somewhat larger, is armed with eight AAMs, including at least four AA-10s.

For interdiction there is the Su-24 Fencer, which has similar low-level, all-weather, terrain-following capabilities to the USAF's F-111, while for ground attack there is the Su-25 Frogfoot, which is in the same class as the A-10 Thunderbolt II, although smaller. It carries around 10,000 lb of offensive weaponry on ten underwing pylons, and its armament includes an internal 30 mm cannon. Added to aircraft such as these are an array of older types, such as the MiG-21 Fishbed and the Su-17/20 Fitter, which serve with other Warsaw Pact air forces.

In recent years the Russians have deployed a large number of strategic air defence systems with capabilities against aircraft at medium and high altitudes; they are currently in the midst of a major effort to improve their capabilities against aircraft and cruise missiles that operate at low levels. This effort includes upgrading their early warning and surveillance systems; deployment of more efficient data-transmission systems and development of new AEW and AWACS aircraft. The Russian AWACS is the Ilyushin Il-76 Mainstay, a variant of the Candid long-range transport; this provides overland and oversea detection of low-flying aircraft and cruise missiles.

One of the most serious developments in the Warsaw Pact's offensive capability is the deployment of large numbers of heavily-armed attack helicopters. The Mil Mi-28 Havoc is primarily an anti-tank helicopter, with some anti-helicopter capability, while another new type, designed by Kamov and given the NATO codename Hokum, is a dedicated fighter helicopter with the primary role of engaging close air support aircraft, including anti-tank helicopters.

Havoc is of conventional appearance and is armed with up to sixteen anti-tank missiles and either a 23 mm or 30 mm cannon; Hokum has co-axial rotors, a streamlined fuselage with a single-seat cockpit in a fighter-like nose, stub wings with ailerons and retractable landing gear. It has no visible anti-tank hardware and is expected to be armed with one or two fixed large-calibre cannon and a battery of air-to-air missiles. The Warsaw Pact forces also have at their disposal a great many Mi-24 Hind helicopter gunships; the latest version is the anti-tank Hind E, armed with AT-6 Spiral missiles. A version of the Hind E without the 12.7 mm Gatling-type gun in the nose, but with a twin-barrel cannon pod attached to its fuselage side, has been named Hind F by NATO. Two basic versions of the Hind exist: the Hind A/B/C assault helicopter, which has a three-man crew, and the anti-tank Hind D/E/F, which has a two-man crew under separate armoured glass canopies in a steel-plated forward fuselage. Both versions have stub wings to carry up to 3,300 lb (1,500 kg) of stores, and eight fully-equipped troops can be carried in the fuselage.

Before examining the RAF's contribution to NATO's defensive structure in Germany in detail, it is advisable to make a brief assessment of the overall threat and the means to counter it. In recent years, Soviet and Warsaw Pact total capabilities have been steadily growing, in terms both of quality and quantity, as Soviet research and development and Soviet resources have been devoted in greater proportions to the military sector of the Soviet economy.

In every category of military force, the Russians have been building a powerful series of strategic and tactical weapons systems. Their military capabilities, as demonstrated by frequent large-scale exercises, give cause for concern by virtue of the advanced technology reflected in the equipment, increased tactical and strategic mobility, the preponderance in front-line divisions and armour, and the very high state of readiness of these forces.

The advantage of exercising the initiative — of choosing the time, place, mode and weight of the attack — is held by the Warsaw Pact. Their geographic advantage of continous interior lines of communication is another significant factor in their favour. These enemy capabilities and the requirements generated by the current NATO strategic concept, with its increased emphasis on the need to be prepared for attacks of varying scales in any region, vividly illustrate the complexity of the tasks facing the air elements of the NATO forces. In the event of war, it is probable that Allied Command Europe's air defence elements, which are continually on alert, would be among the first to engage the aggressor's offensive air thrusts. Aircraft would be employed in a co-ordinated effort with the ground-to-air missile systems deployed throughout ACE. Additionally, the need for timely intelligence during and following an attack would be fulfilled largely by the tactical air reconnaissance forces which are deployed in all regions of ACE.

The main component of the ACE strike/attack force is land based, and is deployed whenever possible on fields facilitating support of the overall mission. The majority of this force is dual capable — in other words, capable of employment in both the conventional and nuclear weapon delivery modes. This fact, plus the inherent flexibility of air power, offers commanders a great many options for the employment of this force. In addition, many squadrons possess a multi-role capability, being able to conduct air defence operations as well as perform the strike/attack role. It is important to point out that the strike aircraft which are maintained at readiness in the nuclear configuration pose a significant deterrent which complements that of the strategic forces.

This peacetime Quick Reaction Alert (QRA) force presents a clear demonstration to a potential aggressor of NATO's capability to escalate a conflict should the need arise. Participation in the maintenance of this deterrent posture, on a round-the-clock basis, by the nuclear-capable air forces of the Alliance, is a very important factor in the Alliance's concept of mutual defence.

Another area where Alliance defence solidarity is put into frequent operational practice, and where the Alliance's air forces play an important role, relates to the ACE Mobile Force, or AMF. This small, highly mobile, multi-national force — capable of playing a deterrent role in any threatened area of Allied Command Europe — comprises both land and air elements and is primarily designed to operate on the northern and southern flanks. The land component, AMF(L), draws troops from seven NATO nations — Belgium, Canada, Germany, Italy, Luxembourg, the UK and the USA. The air component, AMF(A), draws squadrons from Belgium, Germany, the Netherlands, the UK and the USA. While these forces remain under national control at their normal locations, they are assigned specifically to the AMF and must be constantly ready to deploy at very short notice. The land component can be deployed rapidly via the Alliance's airlift capability to any one of several areas within ACE; the attack-capable air element can quickly reinforce the existing Allied Tactical Air Forces in the deployment area.

Until recently, the defence of forward NATO air bases has always been orientated towards surprise conventional air attack. This is still a real threat, and has been countered by the NATO Airfield Protection Programme, which has provided installations such as Hardened Aircraft Shelters (HAS), underground storage facilities for weapons and fuel which are hardened against conventional weapons, and secure personnel accommodation. Today, there is also a significant threat of surprise attack from the ground by SPETZNAZ (Soviet Special Forces) and trained subversive groups. Steps are being taken to meet this threat, but it remains an Achilles Heel within the defensive structure.

The following chapter describes in detail how RAF Germany, as part of the NATO Alliance, is equipped to meet the threat.

# CHAPTER EIGHT
RAF Germany

## 1. Tactical Support Operations

The RAF's principal close support, tactical reconnaissance and short-range interdiction aircraft in Germany is the British Aerospace Harrier GR.5, which is replacing the earlier GR.3. Two Harrier squadrons, Nos. 3 and 4, are deployed at RAF Gutersloh; they would be reinforced, in time of tension, by aircraft of No. 233 (Harrier) OCU from Wittering in the UK. Gutersloh lies in the centre of the British NATO defence zone within the Northern Army Group (NORTHAG), which allows them to cover the 1st British Corps as well as the Dutch, German and Beglian Corps in the NORTHAG area.

Because of its unique ability to operate from small, pre-surveyed sites in the field, and to operate independently of fixed runways, the Harrier is a force-multiplier out of all proportion to the relatively small number of aircraft deployed. At Gutersloh itself, the aircraft are housed in Hardened Aircraft Shelters which were originally built for the Lightnings of Nos. 19 and 92 Squadrons, the base's previous occupants; at a pinch, three Harriers can occupy one HAS. When all the Harriers are at home — which is rarely — Gutersloh is overcrowded; it also houses the Chinooks of No. 18 Squadron and the Pumas of No. 230 Squadron, together with No. 63 Squadron of the RAF Regiment, with eight Rapier fire units. The station is unable to expand, jammed as it is by the River Ems at one end and the town at the other.

For peacetime training the two Harrier squadrons disperse to six pre-surveyed sites, supported by a Forward Wing Operations Centre (FWOC) and two logistics parks. The sites are in the countryside, but in a real war situation would be elsewhere; a Harrier site in a wood is too readily detectable by modern infra-red sensor systems, so a better alternative is to use a bus station, large garage or supermarket on the outskirts of a town. Smash in the frontage, clear out the inside and you have an instant Harrier hide, with a large car park available for short take-off and vertical landing operations (STOVL). Any large buildings can be used: factories, warehouses, barns. Every site of this nature suitable for Harrier operations has been surveyed, and it would take only a matter of hours to prepare it. With East-West tension such as to make war apparently inevitable, no-one would worry too much about damage to civilian property.

Mission tasking for the dispersed Harrier Force comes from the Air Support Operations Centre at 1st British Corps Headquarters via the FWOC, which selects the site and aircraft for the job. Target assignment is worked out between an Army Ground Liaison Officer and the Squadron Authorising Officer; the GLO briefs the Harrier pilots, who are in their cockpits, via a secure telebrief line.

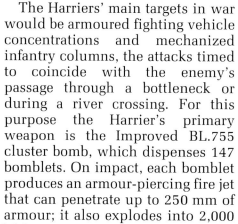

The Harriers' main targets in war would be armoured fighting vehicle concentrations and mechanized infantry columns, the attacks timed to coincide with the enemy's passage through a bottleneck or during a river crossing. For this purpose the Harrier's primary weapon is the Improved BL.755 cluster bomb, which dispenses 147 bomblets. On impact, each bomblet produces an armour-piercing fire jet that can penetrate up to 250 mm of armour; it also explodes into 2,000 fragments, making it a formidable anti- personnel weapon.

In the 1970s, a steerable cluster bomb, the VJ291, was under development to arm the RAF's Harriers and Tornados and give them a stand-off capability. This, however, was cancelled, and so the Ministry of Defence decided to improve the existing BL.755 rather than buy the US Maverick anti-armour missile, stating that an interim weapon was adequate because a stand-off solution was being sought under Air Staff Requirement 1238. A decade later, such an advanced stand-off anti-armour weapon has yet to be brought into service, despite major advances in Soviet armour technology and the increasing sophistication of anti-aircraft weaponry.

The SAM threat to NATO close-support aircraft like the Harrier comes from three types of missile. The SA-13 Gopher, which entered service in 1975, is mounted on a tracked chassis and carries four containerised rounds; it is effective from 50 m to 5,000 m, and has a slant range of 10 km. The Harrier could get below that threat, but a more severe problem would be posed by the man-portable SA-14 Gremlin and SA-16. The former is an IR-homing missile which replaces the older SA-7 Grail; it has an improved seeker, digital guidance electronics, an uprated motor, and a larger warhead. Maximum range is 5 km, and the weapon has a head-on capability against targets manoeuvring at up to 8g. The SA-16 is thought to be faster, longer-ranged and even more manoeuvrable. In addition, the Russians now have a very advanced anti-aircraft artillery (AAA) system in the shape of the new ZSU-X radar-directed twin 30 mm self-propelled gun, which is replacing

Above: A Harrier GR3 of No. 4 Squadron at Gutersloh. By the time these words are read the unit should be in the process of re-equipping with the GR7. *(Robbie Shaw)*
Opposite: A Harrier GR3 as seen through the HUD from the back cockpit of a two seat T4. *(Robbie Shaw)*

the older ZSU-23/4 quadruple 23 mm system.

The need for a stand-off anti-armour weapon is therefore imperative. Late in 1988 the UK Ministry of Defence had narrowed down its choice to meet ASR 1238 to two weapons, the Hunting Swaarm and the Marconi Brimstone. These two systems are now the subject of a two-year early development and risk-reduction exercise; this will enable MoD to finalise the type of system it wants, because the two contenders are considerably different in size, cost and tactical employment. Swaarm, for instance, is designed to attack large formations of enemy AFVs at choke points behind the front line, whereas Brimstone is better used against individual targets — although with further development it should be possible to salvo-fire it, with the missiles locking on after launch. Also, Swaarm's warhead carries sixteen sub-munitions in a large dispenser; these deploy a parachute to produce a helical search pattern, using infra-red and millimetric radar sensors. Once locked on, the sub-munitions home in on the vulnerable top surface of a tank. Hunting claims that Swaarm (Smart Weapon Anti-Armour) will be effective against all Soviet main battle tanks likely to be deployed in the foreseeable future. Brimstone, on the other hand, has a large shaped-charge warhead which, it is claimed, is large enough to penetrate reactive armour, making it unnecessary to attack from above. The missile is an adaptation of the Rockwell Hellfire anti-armour missile used on the AH-64 Apache helicopter, but with a millimetric radar homing head giving it a fire-and-forget capability.

The selected weapon will equip the Harrier GR.5, but will not be available before the mid-1990s. In the meantime, cluster-bomb equipped Harriers must continue to overfly the target, with all the risks this entails. Survival means going in fast and low, and making the maximum use of terrain masking. The trick is not to be seen, and that applies also to countering the air threat from enemy CAP aircraft, because in a war situation the Harriers would be unlikely to have escorts. In this respect the Harrier has a enormous advantage in that it is small and, unlike most modern combat aircraft, does not produce a smoke trail; its disadvantage is a lack of speed over the target, because speed is sacrificed with weapons load.

Providing logistics support for the dispersed Harrier sites up a logistics park, a Royal Engineers team uses bulldozers to scrape out a depression with earth walls called a 'bund'. Into this goes a 680 kg rubberised liner, and then five 1,000 gallon pillow tanks for aviation fuel, which is distributed to the Harrier sites in tankers.

The crewman of this 230 Squadron Puma wearing a Tiger striped cravat — the Tiger is the unit insignia of 230 Squadron. *Robbie Shaw.*

Opposite: Helicopter support for No. 1 BR Corps comes in the shape of Pumas of 230 Squadron and Chinooks of 18 Squadron. One of the latter is illustrated whilst deplaying a Rapier missile unit. *RAF.*

The logistics parks also carry supplies of spares, kerosene, Diesel, compressed gases, food, chemicals, ammunition — in other words, everything necessary to support the Harrier task. One essential item at the moment is a supply of de-mineralised water for the Harrier GR.3's water injection system, which involves piping water from a convenient river or canal and treating it in a de-mineralisation plant in the park. The task has been made a good deal simpler with the advent of the Harrier GR.5, which does not have water injection.

Defending the Harrier sites is also a major operation. The main threat is presented by the Soviet SPETZNAZ special forces; alternatively, the sites could be assaulted by helicopter-borne or paratroop forces. Responsible for setting up an outer defence perimeter around the sites are Nos. 1 and 2 Squadrons of the RAF Regiment's No. 33 Wing, which in the event of a war threat on the Central Front would be reinforced by other RAF Regiment units from the UK and Cyprus. These two squadrons comprise a Quick Reaction Force which is highly mobile and heavily armed, with Scorpion light tanks, Spartan APCs, Sultan armoured command vehicles and Land Rovers. Inner defence is provided by the Harrier Force personnel themselves, who are armed at all times. Ground personnel carry 7.62 mm L1A1 automatic rifles and 9 mm Sterling sub-machine guns, while the Harrier pilots are armed with .45 Browning automatic pistols. Ground Defence Training is a very important aspect of life in the Harrier Force.

Re-equipment with the Harrier GR.5 and the upgraded GR.7 has given the Harrier Force a new ability to hit targets in most weathers and at night; its new systems have increased the prospect of survival in a hostile environment, and it carries a much greater payload over an extended combat radius. Its higher performance, coupled with its Sidewinder AAM armament and built-in cannon, also makes it an effective platform for air-to-air combat, using the well-proven techniques developed over the years with the GR.3.

The Harrier story is far from ended. The next logical step is to produce an advanced STOVL combat aircraft which will have all the Harrier GR.5's attributes, but with a greatly enhanced performance, including a supersonic capability, that will enable it to assume an effective air superiority role in addition to the ground attack task. Such an aircraft has been under study for some years by British Aerospace and McDonnell Douglas, British Aerospace's partner in the STOVL field; in 1973, both companies launched a joint study programme, based on an advanced version of the cancelled P.1154, in response to a US Navy requirement for a supersonic deck-launched aircraft capable of VTOL intercept missions, as well as long-range subsonic strike against surface targets. The design, known as the AV-16S, never moved beyond the Phase 1 study stage due to the predicted development costs versus the available budgets in the USN. However, it was the loss of the AV-16 programme that gave rise in 1975-76 to the Harrier II programme.

From 1975 to 1979, the Hawker Siddeley/British Aerospace team at Kingston continue design studies, together with wind tunnel and model testing, of a number of advanced STOVL (ASTOVL) configurations. These included a study known as the P.1205, which was to have been powered by a Rolls-Royce Pegasus PCB powerplant with about forty per cent more static thrust than the non-PCB engine. However, it was a 1960s design and was out of date for a 1990s application. Other designs followed; these included the P.1214, a forward-swept wing design which avoided the most damaging effects of the high-energy exhaust on those parts of the aircraft aft of, and close to, the Pegasus nozzles. The P.1214 had three vectoring nozzles, the two forward ones with PCB and a single nozzle at the rear.

Later ASTOVL designs, including one designated P.1216, are still very much a reality at Kingston, but present-day work is highly classified. Some interesting facts have emerged, however, and these could point the way to future developments.

In 1983, the UK Ministry of Defence and NASA held a joint symposium to discuss ASTOVL. As a result, four main types of propulsion system were deemed worthy of further investigation; these were vectored thrust with plenum chamber burning (PCB), ejector augmented lift, remote augmented lift system (RALS) and tandem fan. A study phase was initiated, and completed in 1987; the results are now being analysed by both parties.

No definition exists, as yet, of the kind of aircraft that might evolve from such studies. It will most likely be based on the PCB propulsion system, which is the most mature of those under investigation and which gives a one hundred per cent thrust increase for vertical take-off and landing and supersonic flight. It will power a single-seat fighter/attack aircraft in much the same class as the forthcoming European Fighter Aircraft, but with far greater capabilities; the airframe will undoubtedly embody advanced stealth characteristics.

British Aerospace and Rolls-Royce both believe that an ASTOVL combat aircraft could be developed quickly, together with its engine; a prototype could be flying by the mid-1990s. The limiting factor is cost, and the aircraft, like the Harrier, would have to be a joint venture. The potential rewards are enormous.

So, early in the twenty-first century, the RAF could have a multi-role ASTOVL combat aircraft which, in its developed form, would complement and eventually replace EFA. The big question is whether such an aircraft could be afforded in the necessary numbers to deal with multiple air and land threats, which in conventional terms — despite moves to reduce the nuclear arsenals of East and West, and a new surface friendliness — show signs of increasing rather than diminishing.

There is, however, the other end of the scale, and it merits considerable examination. The principal land threat in a conventional war is armour, and will remain so, although the tanks of the twenty-first century might be greatly different from those of today, and capable of a far greater performance. The RAF and the British Army in Germany, like all NATO forces, are deficient in anti-armour aircraft, helicopters and associated weaponry; the only

The main strike element of RAF Germany is the Tornado GR1 with four squadrons at Bruggen and three at Laarbruch. One of the Bruggen squadrons is No. 14 whose aircraft is illustrated on approach to its base.
*Robbie Shaw.*

The first two Tornado squadrons at Laarbruch were 15 and 16. An aircraft from each unit is illustrated in this shot taken at Honington.
*Robbie Shaw.*

fixed-wing aircraft optimised for anti-tank operations in the current NATO inventory is the A-10 Thunderbolt II, which before long will be nearing the end of its fatigue life and which is becoming more vulnerable in the face of the sophisticated forward anti-aircraft systems now being deployed by the Warsaw Pact.

There is therefore a requirement, shared by the RAF and other NATO air arms, for a future battlefield aircraft which would be capable not only of destroying all types of enemy armour — although that would be its main role — but of engaging enemy aircraft and battlefield helicopters as well. In response to this requirement, British Aerospace has designed a remarkable aircraft known as the P.1233, and more popularly as the SABA — Small Agile Battlefield Aircraft.

The SABA project was initiated in 1985, the idea being to design an aircraft that would be capable of operating at low level over the battlefield, engaging helicopters and remotely-piloted vehicles (RPVs), and providing very accurate close support, especially at night and in bad weather. The requirement called for very high agility, and the British Aerospace design team assessed this as the ability to turn through 180 degrees in five seconds at 0.4M. This would enable SABA to meet a fighter in the F-16/MiG-29 class head-on, then turn and shoot an infrared missile before the adversary could get out of missile range.

Assuming that the initial speed of the target was 0.6M, the missile would impact seven seconds later, or twelve seconds after SABA and its opponent passed head-on. This level of agility could be met with a slower aircraft, but British Aerospace's requirement calls for SABA to transit the battle area at 400-450 knots to increase its survival chances. Other requirements include the ability to operate from a 250 metre rough dirt strip and an endurance of more than four hours with a full war load.

British Aerospace considered several airframe configurations. These included the P.1238, a pod and twin-boom layout powered by a single-disc pusher unducted fan; its metal airframe was inherently stable and it would have needed a fly-by-wire system to produce the necessary high agility with carefree handling. Armament was to be six short-range attack missiles, two under each wing and one on each wingtip. Then there was the P.1234-1, designed to be powered by a Rolls-Royce Adour turbofan (the engine that powers the Hawk). When this design was being studied helicopter suppression was seen as the main role, and armament consisted of two air-to-air missiles and a 25 mm cannon in a belly-mounted cupola that could be trained through 360 degrees, the idea being that the aircraft could engage targets throughout a spherical envelope by combining the cannon's 360 degree traverse and the aircraft's 360 degrees of roll. A modified design, the P.1234-3, took this concept a stage further. The instantaneous turn rate was calculated to be forty degrees per second. Instead of a cannon, the turret would fire hyper-velocity missiles from two tubes, with about twelve missiles carried internally. These would be aimed by inputs from three sensor turrets, one in the nose and two mounted dorsally on either side of the fuselage waist. The weapon envelope was plus/minus twenty degrees in pitch in the 360 degree azimuth plane of the aircraft, and a spherical engagement envelope was possible by rolling the aircraft.

The idea was too complex, and the British Aerospace team reverted to a more conventional weapon-launch concept, combing the very highly agile P.1233-1 design with a highly agile dogfight missile. An unducted fan was chosen as the powerplant because of its economical high power, and British Aerospace based performance figures on the 4,501 hp Avco-Lycoming T55 engine. A canard layout was chosen for the design because the inflow to the disc dominated a conventional tailplane, and large elevator or rudder inputs generated only a very small coupling. Pitch control is there fore by means of the canards, with yaw control by the forward-mounted ventral rudder. A dorsal air intake reduces the risk of FOD (Foreign Object Damage) ingestion, while the foreplane and wing vortices ensure a clean flow to the intake at high angles of attack.

The P.1233 is designed to produce a very low radar signature; it will also be quiet, and hard to detect visually. The infra-red signature is also low, and will be reduced even further by anti-IR camouflage paint. The engine exhaust, the primary source of IR detection, is cooled by the airflow and then cooled and dispersed further by passing through the fan.

A 15 Squadron Tornado GR1 in full afterburner at low level.
*Robbie Shaw.*

A former Jaguar unit, No. 20 Squadron is the third Tornado strike unit at Laarbruch.
*Robbie Shaw.*

To sum up, SABA is a very worthwhile concept. It is relatively inexpensive, and would be able to operate from sites almost as restricted as those used by the Harrier. Deployed in numbers, it would give the RAF an unprecedented close-support capability, leaving the Harrier GR.5 Force to concentrate on interdicting targets behind the battle area. The question is not whether the RAF — and perhaps other NATO forces as well — can afford to acquire such an aircraft, but whether it can afford not to.

### Tactical Helicopter Support

RAF Germany has two helicopter units, No. 18 Squadron with Chinooks and No. 230 Squadron with Pumas, both based at Gutersloh. However, the British Army now has a new force, 24 Air-Mobile Brigade, which gives it the capability to deploy a heliborne, fast-reaction force to Germany in a time of crisis. The Brigade, which consists of three infantry battalions, an air defence regiment and a field artillery regiment, is equipped to counter massed enemy armoured movements. The Brigade is airlifted by the RAF's Chinook and Puma helicopters based at Odiham, and these would reinforce the two squadrons in Germany for tactical support operations in NORTHAG. The Pumas will be replaced by EH.101 helicopters in the mid-1990s.

The Brigade held a firepower demonstration in September 1988 before NATO representatives. During this, 550 troops were airlifted by Chinooks and Pumas of Nos. 18 and 230 Squadrons, backed up by Army Lynxes and Gazelles. A three-part battle was simulated to show reconnaissance, main defence, and helicopter armed attack, involving artillery, multi-barrel rocket launchers, machine-guns and minelaying Lynx helicopters. In the reconnaissance phase of the battle, anti-tank Milan and anti-aircraft Javelin missiles were used to destroy the enemy recce force before the main force was deployed.

## 2. Strike and Reconnaissance

RAF Germany has a powerful interdiction/strike component, with seven squadrons of Tornado GR.1s. These are Nos. 9, 14, 17 and 31 Squadrons at RAF Bruggen, and Nos. 15, 16 and 20 Squadrons at RAF Laarbruch.

The principal role of RAF Germany's Tornado squadrons is counter-air, which in practice means carrying out attacks on enemy airfields. For this purpose the Tornado is equipped with the Hunting JP233 sub-munitions dispenser, described in Chapter One. As part of 2 ATAF, RAF Tornados would operate in close concert with Luftwaffe Tornados; the latter carry the MW-1 sub-munitions dispenser, which ejects mines, runway-cratering bomblets and anti-shelter munitions. According to Luftwaffe estimates, up to sixteen hardened aircraft shelters could be destroyed in a single pass, and two Tornados would be enough to render an airfield unserviceable.

The problem with both these systems is that the aircraft is exposed to heavy airfield defences throughout the attack. Modern engineering and repair facilities could soon make an airfield serviceable once more, so attacks would have to be repeated at frequent intervals, with consequent high attrition. This problem was identified by the West German Defence Ministry as long ago as 1978, in a study covering Luftwaffe requirements for the 1990s; the solution was seen as a specialised electronic warfare (EW) aircraft whose function would be to blast a path through the enemy defences, enabling the strike aircraft to reach and attack their targets with a greatly enhanced survival prospect.

By the end of 1984 the tactical requirements for the new aircraft — which would be a version of the Tornado — had been formulated. It would be a multi-role aircraft, able to perform three different tasks: deep penetration reconnaissance, electronic intelligence (ELINT) and defence suppression.

It was realised that the ELINT and defence suppression roles were compatible to a large extent. The ELINT equipment carried by the Electronic Combat and Reconnaissance (ECR) Tornado would enable it to pinpoint the location of radar-directed SAM and AAA threats, which would then be attacked with the appropriate weaponry. The ECR Tornados would therefore serve as pathfinders for the strike formations, guiding them safely through weak spots in the enemy air defence system and, if necessary, using their weapons to eliminate a threat. For this purpose a radar-homing missile system had to be provided which co-operates with the ELINT system; the missile system was to include weapons with infra-red guidance for engaging AAA, as hot gun barrels make excellent targets for IR sensors. In addition, the electronic warfare Tornado would have a 'soft kill' capability, being fully equipped to jam and deceive any radar emitter selectively, not only with its own self-defence ECM pods, but with a dedicated EW pack controlled by the crew.

In June 1986 the Federal German Defence Appropriations Committee authorised the start of the ECR Tornado programme, with a requirement for thirty-five aircraft to be built up to 1991. The first seven were scheduled to enter service late in 1989. The principal difference between the ECR Tornado and the IDS version is that the internal 27 mm cannon are removed to make way for the bulky EW package; the emitter-locator and jamming antennae are flush-mounted in the gun bays, and associated systems are housed in the ammunition storage bins. However, the ECR Tornado can carry all the ordnance specified for the IDS, and can therefore operate in the strike role if necessary.

The ECR Tornado's primary anti-radar missile is the Texas Instruments AGM-88A HARM, which was also offered to the RAF in competition with the British Aerospace ALARM; the latter will eventually equip the RAF's Tornado GR.1s, giving them some defence-suppression capability (see Chapter One). Unlike ALARM, which climbs to altitude and loiters while it searches for a target, HARM homes directly on to its objective at Mach 2 plus; it is fitted with a blast fragmentation-type warhead, optimised for the destruction of radar targets.

HARM operates in three modes: Target of Opportunity (TOP), Prebriefed (PB) and Self-Protect (SP). In the TOP mode, its guidance system detects, locates and classifies radar systems; the information is displayed in the cockpit, enabling the crew to launch HARM towards the highest-priority target. In the PB mode, threat radar locations are loaded in the weapon's computer before the mission. After reaching a pre-determined stand-off launch position — possibly in the target radar's blind zones — the missile can be launched in the general direction of the objective; on reaching a pre-set altitude it scans ahead, identifies radar emissions corresponding to those stored in the computer, and attacks. In the SP mode, HARM's computer is fed information on enemy radar activity picked up by the aircraft's RWR system, and is instantly ready for launch to deal with the threat.

In addition to the Luftwaffe's order for thirty-five ECR Tornados, Italy has declared a requirement for fifteen similar aircraft. The aircraft has also been offered to the USAF as a replacement for the F-4G Phantom 'Wild Weasel' defence suppression aircraft. The Royal Air Force, however, has no stated requirement for the ECR Tornado; in war, the RAF Germany Tornado squadrons would rely for electronic warfare support on the Luftwaffe's ECR Tornados and, where available, the USAF's EF-111 Ravens, which have the primary task of supporting the UK-based F-111 strike force but which would also operate in support of 2 and 4 ATAF. And, of course, the RAF eventually hopes to turn each Tornado into a self-contained defence suppression aircraft, able to carve its own way through the enemy defence barriers with the aid of the Sky Shadow ECM pod and the ALARM anti-radiation missile now being developed by British Aerospace. The Tornado can operate in the reconnaissance role by the addition of the appropriate recce pod, but in RAF Germany tactical reconnaissance is carried out by No.2 Squadron, which converted to Tornados from the Jaguar GR.1 at RAF Laarbruch in 1989.

For air defence, RAF Germany has two squadrons, Nos. 19 and 92, which are equipped with the McDonnell Douglas Phantom FGR.2 and based at RAF Wildenrath. The Phantom still remains an effective air defence system; for long-range interception it carries four Sky Flash AAMs recessed under the fuselage, with four AIM-9L Sidewinders on underwing pylons for close-in combat. The aircraft also carries an internal armament of one 20 mm rotary cannon, with a rate of fire of 6,600 rounds per minute. The aircraft is fitted with the Westinghouse AWG-12 radar which offers several operating modes: pulse-Doppler look-down, pulse air-to-air search and tracking, high/low mapping, air-to-ground ranging, and illumination for the Sky Flash AAM. In the mid-1990s, it is envisaged that the Phantom FGR.2 will be replaced by the European Fighter Aircraft.

Wildenrath is home to RAFG's air defence assets which comprise two squadrons of Phantom FGR2; Nos. 19 and 92. Both used to operate the Lighting, and 19 Squadron aircraft can be identified by the blue and white checks on the RWR. (*Robbie Shaw*).

Airfield defence in RAF Germany is the responsibility of four RAF Regiment squadrons: No. 16 Squadron in Wildenrath, No. 26 Squadron at Laarbruch, No. 37 Squadron at Bruggen, and No. 63 Squadron at Gutersloh. All are armed with the British Aerospace Rapier short-range SAM.

In the event of 2 ATAF airfields being made unusable by air attack, aircraft like the Tornado and Phantom can operate from pre-surveyed stretches of autobahn. Specially-selected straight sections of carriageway have been prepared as emergency runways; trees have been felled on either side, the centre sections concreted over, and refuelling/rearming points set up at either end of the section, served by loop roads. In peacetime, these are picnic and recreation areas.

## 3. The Nuclear Alert Force

RAF Germany has maintained a nuclear quick-reaction alert (QRA) posture since 1958, successively using Canberras, Phantoms and now a proportion of the Tornado strike force. Nuclear tactical air power (TACAIR) is an important factor in NATO's deterrent posture, and has recently become increasingly so with the dismantling of theatre nuclear missile forces, but opinions are divided as to its validity.

Although NATO's first line of defence against conventional attack under the Alliance's agreed strategy is its conventional forces, strategic and tactical nuclear forces contribute greatly to deterrence of both conventional and nuclear attacks. The aim of NATO strategy is to deter attacks at all levels of conflict through a credible defence capability with a mutually supporting triad of conventional, theatre nuclear, and strategic forces; theatre nuclear forces fill what would otherwise be a critical gap between strategic deterrent and conventional forces. This capability is required to avoid the undesirable alternatives of conventional defeat or, worse, escalation to general nuclear war.

The argument for the retention of nuclear TACAIR is that it is desirable politically as well as militarily. For some targets, currently available yield/accuracy combinations for TACAIR would result in target destruction with lower collateral damage that would be the case if missile systems were used. Equally as important is the fact that TACAIR on nuclear alert provides the means whereby the RAF and USAF can participate jointly in the nuclear strike role within the NATO framework. Even though the tactical nuclear weapons (the WE177) available for use by the Tornado Force are of British design and equipped with British warheads, and are therefore completely under UK Government control, they would be released to

A Phantom FGR2 of 92 'East India' Squadron seen on take off armed with Sidewinder and Sparrow missiles. *(Robbie Shaw)*

SACEUR in time of emergency. The sharing of risks and responsibilities involving nuclear strike missions between the RAF and USAF is an important political factor.

The role of the nuclear QRA force, and the nature of its targets, has changed somewhat over the years. It is now a much reduced force, assigned to limited numbers of pre-planned, fixed objectives. Not so many years ago, tactical nuclear weapons would have been needed to ensure the destruction of certain targets — strategically important bridges, for example — that can now be destroyed in a single shot by terminally-guided conventional bombs.

Air interdiction operations are conducted to destroy, neutralise, or delay the enemy's military potential before it can be brought to bear effectively against friendly forces. Deep interdiction attacks do not have an immediate effect on the battlefield situation, but can be of considerable importance in a war of attrition or in areas where the enemy's lines of communication are severely restricted. Therefore, interdiction well beyond the Forward Edge of the Battle Area (FEBA) would be a rather marginal investment of TACAIR during a conflict with the Warsaw Pact; however, shallow interdiction against road and rail communications, or known assembly points, to cut off reinforcements and relieve pressure on the FEBA would have prompt effect and would be particularly appropriate for nuclear TACAIR.

In this context, RAF Germany's nuclear TACAIR force, once released to NATO, would form part of NATO's Follow-On Forces Attack (FOFA) strategy. The Warsaw Pact would enjoy a favourable overall balance of conventional forces at the beginning of a conflict, but the potential strength of NATO would grow over a period of time. Soviet doctrine is therefore based on a rapid strike, taking advantage of NATO's reliance on reinforcement. To maintain the momentum of the offensive, this doctrine calls for the use of follow-on forces which are composed of echelons, reserve forces and Operational Manoeuvre Groups (OMGs). By keeping the momentum of the attack and continuously pouring fresh combat forces on to NATO's defensive positions, the Russians would hope to create major breakthroughs along the defensive to try and destroy the integrity of the defence as a whole. OMGs, which are self-sustaining for a limited period of time, are designed to push through any weakness in the defence and operate independently behind NATO lines to over-run important targets such as command posts, nuclear weapons delivery systems (those placed well forward, that is, such as

The fourth unit at Laarbruch, and the RAF's first Tornado reconnaissance squadron, is No. 2, or to give it its preferred title No. II (AC) Squadron.
*Robbie Shaw.*

tactical rocket batteries and large-calibre artillery) and logistical support complexes. The object is to achieve the rapid collapse of NATO's conventional forces and to prevent the Alliance from resorting to the use of non-strategic nuclear weapons.

If these ground-based nuclear delivery systems were over-run, nuclear TACAIR, operating from bases well to the rear, would remain NATO's only tactical nuclear option. However, it is an expensive one, involving as it does the holding back of numbers of valuable strike aircraft on nuclear QRA when they could profitably be involved in conventional attacks. A part solution, and one which has been practised, is the so-called Dual-Loaded Alert, with both conventional and nuclear weapons loaded on the same aircraft. Although arming an aircraft can be time-consuming, selective down-loading can be correspondingly quick. A Tornado, for example, could have a tactical nuclear store on one pylon and conventional ordnance on the other; if launched for a conventional strike, the nuclear weapon could be down-loaded in less than five minutes, detracting little from the response time. If launched for a nuclear strike, the aircraft would take off with all stores, incurring no delay. The conventional weapons could be jettisoned after take-off, if desired.

Wildenrath based 60 Squadron provides RAF Germany with a limited transport capability using Andover C1 and CC2 aircraft. *(Robbie Shaw)*

This conventional-nuclear QRA mix is a capability uniquely adaptable to TACAIR, since no other weapon system can be launched against an enemy with both nuclear and conventional munitions on board. It has all the advantages of nuclear QRA, plus the flexibility to release conventional resources rapidly for battlefield support.

In summary, NATO is constantly seeking to improve its conventional combat capability to the maximum allowable level dictated by the Alliance's deterrent strategy, a level which will provide a reasonable prospect of frustrating a conventional attack. This in turn will reduce — but not eliminate — NATO's reliance upon a possible nuclear response. As long as nuclear weapons have not been negotiated out of existence, NATO must remain an adequate and appropriate spectrum of nuclear weapons for deterrent purposes. With nuclear weapons in place, an aggressor cannot rely on a relatively cheap and predictable conventional victory. The price of an attack on Western Europe must retain the possibility of triggering an incalculable chain of nuclear escalation. This uncertainty will remain a vital component of NATO's deterrence.

AIR FORCE

# CHAPTER NINE
## The Falklands and Belize

Since the 1982 war with Argentina, Great Britain has maintained a deterrent posture in the Falkland Islands, first of all with Royal Navy aircraft carriers equipped with Sea Harriers, and later with a detachment of No. 23 Squadron Phantom FGR.2s. These aircraft were initially based at Port Stanley, whose runway was lengthened to accommodate them, but moved to Mount Pleasant Airbase when this new airfield complex was completed in 1986. The function of the Phantoms is to provide Quick Reaction Alert (QRA) in order to intercept any intruders into the Falklands Islands Protection Zone (FIPZ), a role in which they are supported by the C-130 Hercules C.1K tankers of No. 1312 Flight. With the re-forming of No. 23 Squadron as a Tornado F.3 unit at RAF Leeming in 1988, the Falklands Phantom detachment is now designated No. 1435 Flight, and personnel are assigned to it from the UK air defence Phantom squadrons.

The RAF's deterrent role in the Falklands is very necessary, for at the time of writing there has been no formal cessation of hostilities between Great Britain and Argentina, and there has been no change in Argentina's aim to annexe the islands in the future. The possibility of a second outbreak of armed hostilities must therefore not be ruled out.

The strategic importance of the Falkand Islands and other British possessions in the South Atlantic — namely the South Shetland and South Orkney Islands, and South Georgia — is that they occupy a strategically dominant position across the Drake Passage, which controls access from the Pacific to the Atlantic — a vital link, because it is the shortest oceanic route between the two oceans, and in the event of the Panama Canal being blocked by armed action or other cause it would become the only route open in the waters of the western hemisphere.

There is another matter of concern, and it is economic. Apart from the recognised fact that the seas around Antartica are rich in fish and marine mammals, many scientists believe that the continent itself and its shelf may be rich in oil, to the extent of giant (half-billion barrel) or supergiant (five billion barrel) fields. Another school of scientific thought, on the other hand, holds that Antartica will not yield any resources of commercial value. Only if oil were discovered in large quantities, making commercial exploitation viable, would the extraction of other minerals such as cobalt, gold and iron — traces of which have been found — become feasible.

141

Nevertheless, even if the commercial value of Antartica proves negligible, no power interested in controlling the access route between the Atlantic and Pacific Oceans can afford to relinquish such control to potentially hostile hands. Why the British Government failed to make the Falklands a secure base before 1982 is beyond the scope of this work, but no time has been lost in turning the islands into a substantial military fortress since then.

The whole policy behind 'Fortress Falklands' is based on deterrence and a posture of flexible response to any threat that might develop to the islands. The threat itself is not difficult to analyse; the Argentine Air Force is pushing ahead with plans to re-equip and restructure by the year 2000, although such plans are at present hampered by trade restrictions, particularly with the United States. In fact, the only significant combat aircraft acquired since 1982 are twenty-two refurbished Mirage IIIs purchased from Israel, and some of these may have been diverted to South Africa as an attrition batch. Negotiations are continuing with Israel for the release of twenty-four A-4 Skyhawks, which are under a US embargo and stored by Israeli Aircraft Industries.

Argentina currently has some forty Mirage IIIs, mainly for interception but some equipped for the reconnaissance role, together with eleven Mirage Vs and twenty-two IAI Daggers for fighter/ground attack. Most, if not all, of these aircraft are now equipped for flight refuelling, the lack of which capability seriously affected Argentina's air operations in the 1982 war. The AAF has two KC-130H tankers, but there are reports that some of the Service's six Boeing 707 transports are being converted to the tanker role. An increased AAR force would give Argentine combat aircraft the capability to attack the Falkands from almost any direction. The AAF also has thirty-one A-4 Skyhawks and sixty-four IA-58A Pucaras for ground attack; the latter are being modified to single-seat configuration, with increased armament.

The Argentine Naval Air Arm now has fourteen Super Etendards, fully equipped with Exocet anti-shipping missiles. Attrition during the 1982 war reduced its A-4 Skyhawk attack force to five aircraft, and sixteen replacements are being held up in Israel by the US embargo. The Navy also has five MB.339 aircraft in the attack role, but serviceability is poor because of a lack of spares for the Viper engines. Argentina is expressing an interest in the Embraer/Aermacchi AMX International attack aircraft, but is making no progress because the aircraft is fitted with the Rolls-Royce Spey engine.

Despite all its problems, Argentina has, on paper at least, around 120 relatively modern combat aircraft which could be used against the Falkands (discounting the Pucaras, which would have to be established at forward bases on the islands themselves.) The question is whether the small RAF deterrent force is sufficient to meet the threat; the RAF believes that it is.

From 1982 until 1986, the Falklands garrison was supplied mainly by sea, with urgent spares, equipment and mail being flown in five times a week by air-refuelled Hercules from Ascension Island, 3,400 nm away. The establishment of the new airfield and military base at Mount Pleasant Airbase (MPA) means that much of the freight and passenger resupply workload has now been taken over by TriStar aircraft of No. 216 Squadron, which make three round-trip flights every week.

With the use of these widebody jets, the rapid reinforcement of the Falklands garrison has entered a new dimension, and has enabled the number of personnel of all three Services — which averaged 4,000 up to 1986 — to be substantially reduced. The British Government's policy is that the Falklands should be adequately defended with the minimum number of forces capable of doing the job; rapid reinforcement, the Ministry of Defence claims, could be achieved within eighteen hours.

During those eighteen hours, the initial air threat would have to be met by the Phantoms of No. 1435 Flight. The number of aircraft deployed in the Falklands is classified, but each Phantom carries a very effective weapons load of two Sky Flash and four AIM-9L air-to-air missiles in addition to its built-in 20 mm SUU-23A Vulcan cannon. In times of tension, the missile load would be increased by the addition of two more Sky Flash, giving each aircraft the

A Harrier GR3 of 1417 Flight about to emerge from its hide at Belize airport.
*(Robbie Shaw Collection)*

capability to engage eight targets with its missiles and then carry out gun attacks.

The role of No. 1435 Flight is to police and if necessary defend the FIPZ, with the additional task of protecting the airhead during a period of tension so that air reinforcement and resupply could continue unmolested. The original 200 nm Total Exclusion Zone around the Falklands has now been replaced by the 150 nm FIPZ, which is patrolled by ships of the Royal Navy, some acting as radar pickets. Radar coverage of the air space beyong the FIPZ is provided by land-based early warning stations, which can detect suspect plots at a sufficient range to give the QRA Phantoms plenty of time to scramble and investigate, or set up a CAP.

Pilots and navigators serve a five-week tour on No. 1435 Flight, as distinct from the normal Falklands tour of four months. The reason for this short tour is that, mainly because of the lack of training facilities, operational efficiency tends to suffer over a longer period. Crews on average fly two sorties each per day, and are rested one day in ten, although the sortie rate can be seriously affected by the weather. Radar contacts approaching the FIPZ occasion three or four QRA scrambles a month, but no aircraft has yet infringed the Zone; the deterrent effect of the Phantoms appears to be a reality.

Using the AAR facilities provided by the Hercules of No. 1312 Flight, Phantoms can remain on CAP for a long time, or alternatively extend their range to meet a threat beyond the FIPZ. The Hercules tankers can be airborne within fifteen minutes of a QRA scramble. In addition to its AAR role, No. 1312 Flight is also responsible for Maritime Radar Reconnaissance within the FIPZ, co-operating closely with the Royal Navy in maintaining surveillance of vessels entering the Zone. The Hercules also carry out mail-dropping sorties to South Georgia, logging surface vessels en route. Other roles include search and rescue and the surveillance of icebergs whose movements may present a threat to shipping.

The aircrews of No. 1312 Flight are drawn from Nos. 24 and 30 Squadrons — Strike Command's strategic transport element of the Hercules Force — at RAF Lyneham. There is plenty of flying, and tasks are varied; in addition to those mentioned above, Hercules crews might find themselves in the target facilities role, giving the Phantom crews a chance to practice low-level interception techniques against transport aircraft. One possible war threat scenario envisages an attempt by Argentine special forces' commandos being dropped on Port Stanley airfield by the AAF's small C-130 force; for this reason Port Stanley airfield is closed to everything except light civilian traffic and most of the main runway rendered unusable by obstacles.

The principal airfield, Mount Pleasant Airbase (also known as RAF Mount Pleasant) is defended by flights of No.26 Squadron RAF Regiment, armed with Rapier SAMs. Each missile site has an eight-man crew, providing round-the-clock air defence coverage. As is usual with Rapier, 100 per cent system reliability is routinely achieved. The Rapier units practise frequent redeployment exercises to prepared sites, the batteries and personnel being airlifted by Chinook helicopter. An additional air defence asset, although hopefully one which will never have to be used, is No. 55 Forward Squadron, Royal Engineers, whose highly efficient runway repair techniques would make the airfield serviceable within hours if the runways suffered serious damage in an enemy air attack.

RAF helicopter support in the Falklands is provided by No. 78 Squadron, with a flight of Chinook HC.1s and a flight of Sea King HAR.3s. Following a recent reduction in the tempo of Phantom FIPZ patrols, two of the Sea Kings have returned to the United Kingdom and are now deployed at RAF Leconfield. Support helicopter operations are mainly carried out by the Chinooks and by Sikorsky S.61s of Bristow Helicopters Ltd, operating under a Ministry of Defence contract, leaving the Sea Kings free to undertake the SAR role. However, the Sea Kings, which are equipped with a cargo-lifting frame of the type used on the Commando Sea King transport variant, also operate in the support role from time to time. Sea King aircrew are drawn from No. 202 Squadron, while Chinook aircrew come from Nos. 7 and 18 Squadrons. Because of

Overleaf: With 78 Squadron badge on the forward fuselage this Chinook is about to lift an underslung load.
*(Robbie Shaw Collection)*
Below: The Phantoms of 1435 Flight at Mount Pleasant have adopted the Maltese Cross as their unit emblem. *(Tony Dixon)*

the threat, all RAF helicopters in the Falklands are fitted with radar warning receivers.

In their present state, it is unlilkely that the Argentine Armed Forces would be capable of mounting an effective assault on the Falklands. That situation might change in the future, but it is far more likely that a negotiated settlement will decide the outcome. Whatever happens, it seems that a strong British presence in the islands must remain an accepted fact; but Britain must at some stage face the need to re-establish friendly relations with Argentina, for the long-term strategic interests of these two allies of the United States coincide in the region. Those interests are: the assurance of free movement throught the Drake Passage, the continued demili-tarisation of the Antartic, and the denial of a hostile military presence in the area, whether on land or sea.

## Belize

As is the case in the Falklands, RAF operations in Belize come under the control of No. 1 Group, Strike Command. The RAF presence in this Caribbean colony has been maintained since early in 1972, as an insurance against hostile action by neighbouring Guatemala, which claims sovereignty. The Royal Air Force Regiment provides point air defence with Rapier SAMs, the key point being Belize Airport; the task is shared on a rotational basis by the various squadrons, which also undertake a good deal of jungle training during their three-month tour of duty. At Sibun — forty-three miles from the sea and down Humming . Bird Highway — both primary and secondary jungle can be found within a few hundred yards of the camp site. Even closer is a forty-foot deep river which provides excellent facilities for practising river crossing techniques. Other survival training is carried out on offshore islands, which form a broken barrier reef between nine and twenty-two miles off the mainland.

An RAF Tactical Communications Wing detachment at Belize Airport provides air traffic control services and an early warning system in conjunction with the RAF Regiment's network of observation posts along the frontier. Offensive and defensive air support is provided by a detachment of four Harriers, operated by air and ground crews on rotation from the UK. The small Harrier force is designated No. 1417 Flight. Troop and equipment transport duties are undertaken by four Puma helicopters of No. 1563 Flight, operated by personnel of the Odiham Wing. In addition, the Belize Defence Force Air Wing, formed in 1983, operates two Britten-Norman BN-2B Defenders on border patrol, reconnaissance and liaison duties.

Helicopter support for the British forces in the Falkland Islands is provided mainly by 78 Squadron, consisting of a small number of Sea King HAR3s and Chinooks HC1s. This photograph was taken at Stanley, shortly before the move to Mount Pleasant.
*Robbie Shaw Collection)*

# CHAPTER TEN
## Operational Training and Exercises

In order to fulfill its commitments, in both war and peace, the Royal Air Force must exercise continually, developing and refining its skills throughout the whole spectrum of operations. It is worthwhile examining some typical recent exercises, because they give an indication of how the present-day RAF would react in a given war situation.

In November 1987 the RAF, Royal Navy and Army all took part in the Exercise Purple Warrior, which was designed to recreate some of the strategic problems encountered during the Falklands War, but with a different political and tactical scenario. One of the central features of the exercise was the deployment by sea to the 'combat zone' of the RAF Harrier GR.3s; another was the exercise of command and control over these aircraft and others, including helicopters, once they were established ashore. The area chosen for the exercise was Galloway, in the south-west of Scotland.

Purple Warrior was a 'Services-Protected Evacuation' of UK nationals and dependents from a Commonwealth country, the fictitious island group of Kaig, a notional 1,500 nm from the UK. Kaig had been threatened by an unfriendly neighbour whose 'Orange Forces' might attempt to invade, so a strong force was despatched both to assist in the evacuation and to deter aggressors. Some 20,000 service personnel took part, only slightly fewer than during the initial combat phase of the Falklands campaign.

Unlike the Falklands conflict, which was run almost exclusively by the Royal Navy and Royal Marines, Purple Warrior was run by the Royal Navy and the Army. In overall command of the task force was Admiral Sir Julian Oswald at his HQ at Northwood, Middlesex. The ground and air forces, once on land, came under the control of Major General Nick Vaux's Joint Force HQ in the exercise area itself. The RAF Harrier GR.3 detachment from No. 1 Squadron at RAF Wittering would operate under his ultimate control once established ashore. The Harriers would be tasked to carry out offensive support, air defence missions and air reconnaissance during the evacuation and subsequent expected hostilities and then withdraw back to the UK.

On 2 November the RAF Harriers embarked aboard HMS *Ark Royal* in Portsmouth, six aircraft with some sixty pilots and maintenance personnel. The seventy-two support personnel, including the No. 1 Squadron Recce Intelligence Centre (RIC) and and RAF Regiment team for air and ground defence, embarked in the chartered ferry *Tor Scandinavia* on 4 November. Like the ferry *Norland* in 1982, *Tor Scandinavia* was one of the many Ships Taken Up From Trade (STUFT) to boost the sealift capability of the amphibious force.

Aboard HMS *Ark Royal* during the passage north, the six RAF Harriers carried out combat air patrols in company with the Sea Harriers of No. 801 Naval Air Squadron. For a number of years now, No. 1 Squadron pilots have undergone periodic refresher training in carrier launch and recovery techniques, using the ski-jump at the Sea Harriers' Yeovilton base and carrying out deck landings and take-offs from the carriers themselves. This part of their training is unique within the Harrier Force, but is a vital part of No. 1 Squadron's task. The Squadron could find itself flying and fighting literally anywhere in the world, from northern Norway as part of the SACEUR Strategic Reserve to Belize, or in a Falklands-type war situation. As a result, aircrew familiarisation with carrier techniques was quick and trouble-free; not so, however, with the maintainers.

One of the purposes of this exercise from No. 1 Squadron's point of view was to establish under realistic conditions exactly what spares holdings and what mix of specialist maintainers was most appropriate to a deployment of this kind. As in the Falklands campaign, most of the Squadron's logistic tail with the heavy engineer equipment was based on a separate ship. Not to put too fine a point on it, there is no guarantee that the other ship will survive the passage to the war zone, so if this ship and its personnel are lost (as was the MV *Atlantic Conveyor* in May 1982) there must be a core of specialists aboard the carrier who can make do and mend with the facilities available from the Fleet Air Arm.

The Squadron admits that it learned a lot during this phase of the exercise. Harrier GR.3 availability was as near to 100 per cent at all times as it was possible to get, and the lessons learned will mean that this level of availability will be easier to sustain in future operations. The logistic burden was eased by the fact that the Harrier and Sea Harrier are very similar in many important areas, so manpower and spares resources could be pooled if necessary to surmount difficulties. This logistic flexibility is unique to the Harrier family.

D-Day was set for 9 November. The assault began at dawn with a simultaneous paratroop drop on West Freugh airfield by the British Army's 5th Airborne Brigade, using Hercules drawn from all four squadrons of the Lyneham Wing, and an amphibious assault by the Royal Marines of 3 Commando Brigade on the eastern side of Loch Ryan. By mid-morning West Freugh was secure and the first flights

A typical strafe target on a range, in this case Donna Nook. An acoustic sensor is buried in the ground at the base of the target, and this determines the pilot's score. RAF ranges are frequently used by USAFE and NATO aircraft. *(Robbie Shaw)*

of an almost continual shuttle service of Hercules were bringing in equipment. Once the Royal Marines were established ashore and making good progress down to West Freugh and a disused airfield nearby at Castle Kennedy, the logistic effort was transferred to West Freugh itself. Sea King helicopters from the assault ship HMS *Intrepid* began the laborious process of moving Javelin SAM teams and, later, Rapier air defence units ashore to protect the airhead, assisted by Chinooks and Pumas of Nos. 7 and 33 Squadrons. The latter had flown 400 nautical miles from RAF Valley, Anglesey, which was deemed to be another aircraft carrier for the purpose of the exercise.

It was at this stage that the learning curve became very steep. In the Falklands, operations ashore were under the command of HQ 3 Commando Brigade, which made communications simple and quick; Purple Warrior, as a tri-service exercise with two distinct landing areas at Loch Ryan and West Freugh, had a rather more complicated command structure and the inevitable and understandable conflicts in priorities between the three services, and even between separate arms of the same service, created the sort of problems that an exercise of this kind exists specifically to show up. What was most apparent was need to satisfy urgent requirements in order of priority.

The first of these was the deployment of Javelin man-portable SAMs and Rapier missile batteries to protect the airhead through which the evacuation and much of the reinforcement would take place. The next was provision of fuel supplies for the aircraft using the airhead; equally important was the establishment ashore of the land-based aircraft, their logistic support and their co-located operations and tasking cells. All this was done, and in the correct order, but it took time. It was not until 12 November, for example, that the Harrier GR.3s were fully self-continued in their forward operating base (FOB) at West Freugh.

Once they were installed, however, the Harriers got on with their job very efficiently. Offensive air support missions were carried out all over the exercise area, the GR.3s carrying a typical load of two AIM-9L missiles and three BL-755 cluster bombs but no external fuel tanks. For recce purposes the nose-mounted cameras were used to gather air intelligence and target information, the information being disseminated through the RIC.

Air defence remained a priority throughout the exercise as the Orange Forces were expected to (and did) mount low-level attacks; these were flown by Jaguars of Nos. 6 and 54 Squadrons from RAF Coltishall, and Buccaneers of the Lossiemouth Strike Wing. Primary air defence duties were carried out by the Phantoms of No. 43 Squadron, which based itself at West Freugh. They mounted CAP at a range of about 80 nm upthreat from the FOB, covering the valleys which would be the most logical avenues of approach for hostile aircraft attacking from any given direction. the Sidewinder-armed Harriers carried out CAP sorties at a range of some 40 nm, providing defence in depth and covering other possible avenues of approach.

Much of the time a mixed fighter force of two Harriers and two Phantoms operated together on CAP, the Phantoms using their air intercept radars to detect incoming hostiles and then both types vectoring on to the threat. Yet again a lot was learned, not the least of which was that in-flight refuelling could be dispensed with, if necessary, by the Harriers. Refuelling probes were taken to Scotland, but not used as there were no tankers available. The lack of air-to-air refuelling did not seem to affect the fuel-efficient Harrier Force if it operated with external tanks. This was a considerable asset to the defence in depth; the Harriers, when lying well back from the Phantom CAP areas, were able to cover the alternative routes used by any enemy fighters which might have evaded the initial air defence screen. The concept of a mixed fighter force was proven to be highly effective, the Phantoms' radars providing a force-multiplier effect which permitted the most economical use of scarce Harrier assets.

As far as the business of supporting the ground forces and operating from an austere site was concerned, very few lessons were learned; No. 1 Squadron had been practising dispersed operations for a long time. Only in one aspect did the deployment differ from the usual procedure; instead of operating from dispersed, camouflaged hides off the airfield, the Harriers were constrained to operate from the main runway at West Freugh, with the aircraft dispersed on temporary steel mesh surfaces around the airfield perimeter. For the purpose of this exercise there seemed little point to the planners in complicating the logistic setup unnecessarily by going on to a full war footing.

What was important on Purple Warrior was, firstly, to get the aircraft and their first-line support on to the ground using whatever means were available and, secondly, doing it quickly. The exercise was not intended solely to test the Harriers in their primary role of offensive air support from dispersed bases; among other things, it was an exercise in the command and control from a tri-service headquarters of the Harrier force in a war-like environment during out-of-area operations.

### Exercise Elder Forest

Exercise Elder Forest, which is usually held in the spring, is the annual UK air defence exercise, involving some 180 UK-based fighter aircraft and about 48,000 personnel. The scenario is classic: several weeks of tension, with both NATO and Warsaw Pact forces on full alert, followed by the outbreak of war. All-out hostilities are preceded by attacks on key points and personnel by SPETSNAZ (Soviet Special Forces) groups; then a NATO AWACS, assigned to No. 11 Group for the purpose of the exercise, reports formations of enemy aircraft inbound over the north Norwegian Sea and the Baltic. Details of the threat are instantly passed by datalink from the AWACS computers to HQ RAF Strike Command at High Wycombe, and to other key radar ground stations on the British mainland. The threat is simulated by UK-based strike aircraft and by aircraft of other NATO air forces. France's Armée de l'Air also takes part; the exercise provides excellent training for its Mirage IV force, which in time of war would have to penetrate enemy air space at low level to launch its nuclear-tipped ASMP (Air-Sol

Moyenne Portée) missiles. During the exercise, hostilities escalate rapidly, until on the third day the scenario is that the United Kingdom is coming under heavy and persistent conventional, nuclear and chemical/biological air attack.

As part of the exercise, the Jaguars, Tornados and Harriers of the Strike Command Offensive Support Force deploy to Norway, Denmark and Germany; they then become part of the Aggressor Force, simulating the enemy in attacks on airfields, radar sites, ports, logistics installations, oil refineries and $C^3$ centres. All these must be defended by the interceptor squadrons of No. 11 Group. The work-up to the exercise proper lasts for some weeks, the fighter squadrons honing their skills in simulated combat with one another.

### Exercise Mallet Blow

Exercise Mallet Blow, which is held over the Otterburn training range in Northumbria, is held four times a year and is designed to permit RAF and NATO aircrew to practise attacks on ground targets, to provide realistic training for attacking aircrew, air defence fighter squadrons, communications and jamming personnel, and SAM units. Participating air forces are usually the RAF, USAF, Royal Danish Air Force and the Luftwaffe, resulting in a mixture of Tornado GR.1s, Jaguars, Harriers, Buccaneers, F-16s and F-111s. Organisation starts about two months before the exercise, when the RAF formally invites other air forces to take part. The targets are set up by a team composed of RAF and Army personnel; two ranges designated Bravo and Charlie are used, and are alternated daily during the week-long event.

Bravo is the interdiction range. Pilots are tasked to aim at a bridge or at one or more of the seventy-plus derelict vehicles scattered across the firing area to represent a deployed motorised infantry regiment. Charlie is the counter-air range, and is equipped with a simulated runway and SAM site. The placing of targets is restricted, because Otterburn is a National Park area; this causes some problems for the organisers when it comes to updating and improving the range so that the aircrew can practise new tactics. One result is that experienced aircrew tend to view Mallet Blow as a routine chore; on the other hand, newcomers find the experience a challenge, and very useful in developing tactical skills.

Aircraft are allocated time on target slots by Strike Command and enter the range singly or in formations of up to eight. Because environmental restrictions forbid the use of live munitions all weapons are inert, usually consisting of small practice bombs that produce a flash and/or smoke for visual reference and scoring. The Harriers fire rockets, other RAF aircraft drop 1,000 lb retarded bombs, and the USAF drops 500 lb retarded bombs.

Around 170 sorties are flown each day, the attacks being recorded on video. The tapes are sent to the relevant units after the exercise so that the pilots can assess their own attacks, and

The result of a strafing run by a USAFE A-10 on Donna Nook range. There is so much sand thrown up that the target can almost be obliterated.
*(Robbie Shaw)*

compare them with the way other pilots use the terrain on their approach to the target. Each aircraft's score is radioed to Strike Command immediately after the attack, then relayed to the pilot's base. Scores between squadrons and air forces are not officially compared; the exercise is purely tactical, with the emphasis on creating a realistic wartime environment. Aircraft participating in Mallet Blow also have to elude air defence fighters — Tornado F.3s, Phantoms and Hawks — as they transit to the target areas via the low-level routes.

### Exercise Red Flag

Red Flag, which has been described as the most realistic simulated warfare exercise in the world, is controlled and administered by the USAF Tactical Fighter Weapons Center at Nellis Air Force Base, Nevada, which is responsible for conducting advanced tactical fighter training and combat training under simulated war conditions for the USAF, US Navy, NATO and other allied air forces. RAF strike aircraft participate from time to time in Red Flag, which was set up in 1972 in an attempt to remedy tactical deficiencies revealed during the Vietnam War.

The Red Flag operating area covers some ten million acres, reserved for military flying, in which three million acres constitute the actual range area. This range includes fifty different types of target, including airfields and industrial complex outlines, two vehicle convoys (one of which is more than seventeen miles long, correctly spaced and protected by tracked anti-aircraft guns), ten miles of railway with a ten-car train, and armoured replicas of Soviet main battle tanks. These targets are defended by thirty-five threat simulators which are similar visually (and in most cases electronically) to Soviet-built equipment. Organised into two Brigades, early warning radars detect aircraft at 300 miles and pass data to the Red Force filter centre at the Range Control Centre. The Filter Centre in turn relays this information to Red Force Brigade Commanders who order defensive operations.

More than fourteen different types of radar unit simulate those used by Warsaw Pact countries, operating at the same frequencies, pulse widths, pulse repetition rates, scan patterns and power levels. TV cameras are fitted to many of these units to cover the same area as the radar; other instruments report threat switch positions and transmit to Range Control. All data collected on the range is processed by computers which can generate not only plots of an engagement or of a single aircraft's entire mission, but also several different kinds of two- or three-dimensional graphic displays from different perspectives.

The Nellis Range offers capabilities far beyond those normally associated with a bombing or gunnery range. It goes a long way towards creating a real-time war situation without employing AG or AA weaponry. When pilots return from a sortie, the Range Control Centre provides computer plots of the mission. Pilots can watch video tapes of their aircraft as seen in the sights of enemy surface-to-air missiles, anti-aircraft guns or camera-gun film shots by aggressor aircraft. Two squadrons, the 64th and 65th of the 57th Tactical Training Wing at Nellis, fly the F-16 in the aggressor role.

## Exercise Maple Flag

Much of the RAF's combat training overseas has now switched to Canada, where Exercise Maple Flag combines the realism of Red Flag with the more European (and specifically northern European) environment of Canada. The exercise is centred on the Cold Lake Air Weapons Range, Alberta, and is run by Red Flag personnel. It is laid out on the same lines as the Nevada range, with simulated SAM and AAA sites and dummy armour. The range, which measures 100 miles by 40, is virtually flat, presenting a real challenge for low-level pilots used to terrain-masking techniques. Concealment is a problem, as a camouflaged Tornado flying over a frozen lake is easily sighted by aggressor aircraft. The nature of the terrain also makes target detection difficult, the camouflaged sites and dummy AFVs among the trees presenting tough objectives to pilots flying at 150 feet and 500 knots.

As in Red Flag, the exercise begins with a composite strike mission involving large numbers of aircraft performing attack, reconnaissance, combat air patrol, escort and defence suppression tasks. After more missions, a second composite demonstrates the effectiveness of the training. Participating aircraft are switched from the Blue Forces (attackers and escorts) to Red Forces (air defence CAP). Maple Flag also includes search and rescue missions, and pilots listed as shot down are flown out to the range to undergo a period of survival training before being picked up by SAR helicopter.

## Air Combat Training

The fighter squadrons of No. 11 Group (including the Tactical Weapons Units) and RAF Germany send detachments periodically to the NATO Air Combat Manoeuvring Instrumentation Range at Deccimommannu, in Sardinia, which became operational in 1979 under the auspices of USAFE for the combat training of NATO fast jet fighter pilots. Decci is one of twelve similar ranges throughout the world, and currently the only one in Europe. Together with its counterparts, the facility provides fighter pilots with the opportunity for aggressive fighter combat in a realistic scenario without requiring special targets, live missiles, or, more importantly, the possible loss of a pilot or an aircraft.

The range itself is a 30 nm diameter circle over the sea about 50 nm off the west coast of Sardinia, with a base height of 5,000 feet and a ceiling of 50,000 feet. Any aircraft straying from the circle, unless transiting to or from the range, can be recalled to base by the local coastal radar at Mirto. This applies particularly to the adjacent NW area outside the range, where there is a civilian air route.

The ACMI consists of four principal interfaced elements. The first is an Airborne Instrumentation Subsystem (AIS), a pylon-attached transponder pod with locking and connection points identical to those of the AIM-9 Sidewinder and linked to the aircraft's electrical, avionic and weapon systems. The AIS pod communicates directly with equipment in four thirty-five-ton buoys — the Tracking and Communications Subsystem (TCS) —

moored at sea beneath the range, one in the centre and the others around the circumference. Two additional land-based monitoring units located on mountains to the north and south of Decci complete the remote part of the TCS.

The information is passed to the land-based TCS master station situated some 4,000 feet up a mountain north of Decci and from there fed by microwave to the Computer and Computation Sub-system (CCS) at Decci. This processes the data received from each aircraft: altitude, speed, bearing, angle of attack, what types of missiles are programmed into it. It also calculates the range and simulated track of a missile in relation to the dynamic track of its selected target.

From the CCS computers, the data is passed to two six feet square graphical VDU screen displays above the Range Training Officer's (RTO) console; these can be watched by an audience of about twenty. It is the responsibility of the RTOs to monitor the exercise, vector the pilots to the opposition (saving range time and simulating ground radar control) and to have radio contact with their own pilots. Not only can the audience see the aircraft in plan view, but the image can be rotated through ninety degrees to give an elevation. Furthermore, a second screen, which is normally used for an alpha-numeric display of the aircraft data, can be used to show a graphical cockpit view of any combatant.

When an aircraft is 'killed' a coffin-shaped outline appears around it and its pilot is vectored out of the fight by his RTO for forty-five seconds, at which point he is free to return and the coffin is removed. During this period the computer will not recognise, and therefore not record, any missile launch or gun firing from the killed aircraft. The length of combat time over the range is strictly controlled to twenty-minute slots for the aircraft using the facility. At the end of their slot the pilots return and debrief, using a video recording of the combat at the Display and Debrief Subsystem (DDS). They can freeze a frame or play back to identify mistakes, lost opportunities and incidents during the range slot to get a clear and complete overall picture of the combat.

The use of Deccimommanu is of great value, but it is expensive. the RAF's annual slot allocation is for 996 half-hour periods which can accommodate about 2,400 individual sorties. The slot rental fee is about £3,000 each at 1988 prices, but to this must be added the cost of transit to and from Sardinia, plus the transport of support personnel.

In July 1988 a European industrial consortium led by British Aerospace — working under a munitions control licence from the US State Department — placed a $50 million contract with Cubic for the establishment of an ACMI range in the North Sea some 80 nm off the UK coast east of the Humber. The range, which has a diameter of 30 nm, is run under the supervision of the RAF, R.Neth.AF and USAFE. British Aerospace leases hour-long 'slots' to the three air forces, and the range may also be opened to other European NATO air forces.

The centre of the range has one master tower with a tracking and instrumentation station, plus five remote tracking and instrumentation stations placed around the circumference. The remotes are linked radially to the master tower by fibre-optic cables buried under the sea bed. The system operates exactly the same way as that at Decci, participating aircraft being fitted with AIS pods. The range is controlled from RAF Marham in Norfolk, with display and debriefing centres at RAF Coningsby in Lincolnshire, RAF Bentwaters in Suffolk, R.Neth.AF Leeuwarden and R.Neth.AF Soesterberg. The system, which achieved initial operational capability in April 1990, can handle thirty-six aircraft simultaneously, although there are plans to expand this to forty-five.

With the RAF alone requiring an estimated 1,400 range slots by 1991 — not counting usage by Hawks in their war role, or offensive support aircraft — the North Sea ACMI system will prove crucial, on grounds of both efficiency and cost saving in the long term.

RAFG Tornados often deploy at Goose Bay in Canada for low flying training. They also take the opportunity to participate in the annual Maple Leaf exercise at Cold Lake, where they operate alongside Canadian and USAF aircraft, such as the F-18 and F-16. *(Robbie Shaw)*

### Low-Level Flying Training

Apart from air displays, nothing focuses public attention on the activities of the Royal Air Force more than low flying, especially when it results in a fatal accident. In the six years between January 1982 and December 1988 the RAF lost thirty-nine aircraft (fifteen Jaguars, seven Tornados, six Hawks, five Harriers, three Phantoms and three Buccaneers) in accidents directly related to low-level training in the United Kingdom and Germany. Twenty-three aircrew lost their lives; the fact that others survived says a great deal for the efficiency of Martin-Baker ejection seats.

There are two problems associated with low flying. The first is that it is a high-risk business, leaving little latitude for error when an aircraft is flying at 250 feet and 480 knots — the minima laid down for training on the UK low-level routes — and still less when it is flying at 100 feet and 600 knots, as is sometimes the case over unrestricted sea areas. The second problem is an environmental one; people are understandably disturbed by high-speed aircraft passing overhead at low altitude, and the possible consequences to civilian life and property in the event of an accident. Fortunately, no accident involving low flying by an RAF aircraft has yet resulted in the loss of civilian lives; the low-level routes are carefully planned to avoid built-up areas, and isolated farms in, say, the Lake District are treated as SAM sites, with action taken to fly round them.

To reduce the risk of collision at low level, traffic separation has been operating around the UK low-level network since October 1988. The decision to institute this was taken by the UK Ministry of Defence following the loss of two RAF Tornado GR.1s in a mid-air low-level collision earlier in the year. Separate days are now allocated between Strike Command, RAF Germany and the US Air Force; traffic is well separated and moved in a broadly clockwise direction around the UK system. A computerised notification and warning system, based on a central computer with a large network of terminals linking each squadron, is also being brought into operation; the interactive system will accept notification of sortie details and in return give details of warnings and restrictions in low-flying areas. To reduce the risk of collision still further, particularly at night and in poor weather, the RAF's Harriers, Jaguars, Buccaneers and Hawks are fitted with high-intensity strobe lights; these will also be retrofitted to the Tornado GR.1 force over the next few years.

Accidents at low level, despite the stress and workload involved in this kind of flying, are by no means all attributable to pilot error, as the following examples — all taken from the 1987 record — show.

On 22 April, a pair of Buccaneers of the Lossiemouth Strike Wing were operating at night off Scotland. Having let down to 600 feet and split up for an attack on a simulated ship target, the navigator of the No. 2 aircraft called for a confirmation of the leader's attack heading. About four seconds later the lead crew saw a fireball as the No. 2 hit the sea. Both crew were killed; the cause of the accident has not been determined, although pilot error may have been to blame in this instance.

On 17 June a reconnaissance Jaguar, with another Jaguar as chase, was flying east across a range of hills in the Lake District, transiting between targets. A pair of Tornados was approaching from the south at low level; these turned left to avoid overflying the town of Keswick and its hospital, both of which are designated as noise-sensitive areas, and a nearby hang-gliding site. The Jaguar crossed a high ridge and collided with a Tornado coming from the opposite direction. The Jaguar pilot was killed; the two Tornado crew ejected, though both were injured.

A week later, on 24 June, a Jaguar QFI was acting as bounce to a pair of Jaguars operating at low level in Wales. On the third bounce the Jaguar turned in hard, was seen to wobble and then depart. The pilot ejected just before impact, but he was outside the seat envelope and was killed.

On 27 July, a Tornado was operating at low level over Yorkshire when the pilot saw a fete in progress in a field near a village adjacent to his route. To avoid any noise nuisance he gently pulled up to 1,500 feet. As he eased forward to return to low level, the controls locked. Both crew ejected at 800 feet from the diving aircraft. The total elapsed time from the first control malfunction warning was less than nine seconds.

On 26 August, three F-4J Phantoms of No. 74 Squadron set out from RAF Wattisham to carry out practice interceptions (PIs) over the North Sea. However, because of poor weather the sortie was diverted to Wales, where the weather was better. During an intercept on a Tornado, and while turning towards some hills, one of the Phantoms flew into rising ground, killing both crew.

On 2 November, two Harrier GR.3s were Nos. 3 and 4 of a six-ship formation tasked with carrying out a co-ordinated attack on Otterburn Range, Northumberland. From the initial point (IP), even-numbered aircraft were to follow a track almost direct to the target, while the odd-numbered aircraft were to take a slightly longer offset route to achieve a sequenced separation of the aircraft over the target. The attack order was to be 2, 1, 4, 3, 6, 5. No. 2 overflew the target, and No. 1 attacked eight seconds later. After a sixteen-second delay Nos. 3 and 4 attacked simultaneously. The aircraft collided almost directly over the target and impacted very shortly afterwards, killing both pilots.

The accident was seen by several witnesses and recorded on video tape, enabling the investigation to discount the weather or other natural operating hazards. Both aircraft appeared to be under control until the collision, so pilot incapacitation seemed an unlikely cause. The investigation concluded that the pilots failed to avoid each other as briefed, with three major contributory causes that resulted in the accident. It was conceived as a visual plan, but in effect it was not; it required a degree of precision in its execution which was difficult to achieve; and the final safety measure of briefed collision avoidance responsibilites was liable to be compromised through distraction.

Much of the RAF's Tornado training at night and in bad weather is carried out in Labrador, but regular monthly training is carried out in the European environment. Pressure on UK low-level airspace is increasing all the time, primarily because German airspace — where a lot of RAF low-level training has been carried out — carries the densest air traffic in the world. In 1987, for example, NATO air forces made a total of 690,000 flights over the Federal Republic from their air bases in that country alone; these included about 60,000 low-level flights by day and night. German rules governing low flying are strict; aircraft are restricted to an altitude of between 490 and 1,480 feet (150 and 450 metres), flights at lower levels being permitted only over seven training areas. Despite attempts to spread the low-flying burden among other European NATO allies, Britain remains the only other nation with a recognised low flying system.

Low-level flying training is more than an essential part of the RAF's operational techniques; in a world of sophisticated radar, SAMs and AAA, it is a recipe for survival. To be an effective deterrent the RAF's offensive support squadrons must train where they need to fight — at low level, by day or night, in good weather and bad. But every year, the RAF and other NATO air forces are compelled to share Europe's air space with an increasing number of other users: commercial airlines, general aviation, gliders, hang-gliders, microlights, parachutists, balloons — and, of course, birds. Add to this restricted air space over populated areas and around busy military and civilian airfields, weapons ranges and training areas, all of which have to be circumnavigated by a fast-jet crew who might fly a low-level sortie from one end of the British Isles to the other in less than an hour, and one begins to realise the stress and pressures involved. In fact, it can only be a tribute to the skill of the RAF and NATO aircrews that the overall accident rate remains as low as it is. In 1987 the overall RAF accident rate was 0.28 accidents per 10,000 flying hours, the lowest ever.

## Competitions and Overseas Deployments

One measure of an air force's efficiency is to compete on equal terms with other air arms, and to achieve consistently good results. Since the early 1960s, the RAF has regularly competed in the Strategic Air Command Bombing Competition in the United States, and has just as consistently won trophies in the face of formidable opposition. In 1984, the RAF's Tornado GR.1 took part in this prestigious contest for the first time, in competition with USAF and RAAF entrants.

The Tornados were from No. 617 Squadron at RAF Marham, Norfolk, supported by Victor K.2 tankers of No.55 Squadron, from the same base. The Curtis E. LeMay bombing trophy, which is awarded to the bomber crew compiling the most points in high-and low-level bombing and time control, was won by one Tornado crew, another finishing in second place; altogether forty-two crews took part, the RAF competing against USAF F-111 and B-52 crews, and RAAF F-111s. The John C. Meyer memorial trophy, awarded to the F-111 or Tornado team compiling the highest damage expectancy from their bombing, was won by a team comprising two Tornados. Their scores were assessed on both low-level bombing and evasive tactics using ECM. Third place also went to a Tornado team. In the

Mathis Trophy, awarded to the unit with the highest points for both high- and low-level bombing, the RAF crews who won the Meyer Trophy came second, with twenty-one teams competing. It was the first time that teams from outside the United States had won the LeMay or John C. Meyer trophies, although in 1974 RAF Vulcans won the Mathis Trophy.

Apart from low-level — 500 feet (153 metre) — sorties, the competition also included high-level — 15,000–20,000 feet (4572–6096 metre) — legs with flights of several hours over 1,500–2,000 miles. This meant that the Tornados proved their lethal bombing accuracy in missions for which they were not specifically designed, and which put them at the disadvantage of being the only aircraft in the contest. The competition was spread over eight weeks and involved attacks on targets and intercept evasion at low level over ranges in Nevada, Wyoming, Montana and South Dakota, sometimes 900 miles from their operating base. It was in two phases; the first involved dropping a 3 kg bomb on each of two targets, neither of which was visible to the crews, who had to use offset blind bombing techniques. They also had to evade a simulated ground-to-air attack by SA-2 and SA-4 missiles and a fighter attack. The Tornados used their Sky Shadow ECM pods to provide the necessary countermeasures.

In the second phase, night and day sorties utilised simulated electronic bombing, with scoring tracked from the ground. These sorties took an average of five hours and involved several mid-air refuelling rendezvous which required split-second accuracy to avoid losing penalty points. Normally, Tornado sorties would average less than two hours, so the increased flying time was an unfamiliar — and valuable — experience for the crews. Again during these sorties, the aircraft had to evade simulated SA-2 and SA-4 attacks.

The 1985 SAC Bombing Competition was even tougher, and once again the RAF Tornados — this time from No. 27 Squadron of the Marham Wing — performed outstandingly well, with the support of the Victor K.2s of No. 57 Squadron. The Tornado crews were placed first and second in both the Curtis E. LeMay and John C. Meyer Trophies, and second in the Mathis Trophy, the sorties lasting over six hours with AAR. Thirty-four teams took part, and again the method of scoring in the competition was based on timing, accuracy of navigation, ECM techniques, fighter and SAM evasion and damage expectancy. Although the Tornados performed

Below: A 16 Squadron Tornado GR1 about to depart Cold Lake for a combined Tornado/F-16 mission during a Maple Flag exercise. *(Robbie Shaw)*

Above: RAF aircraft frequently take part in exercises overseas, such as the Red Flag at Nellis, Nevada. One of the first types to participate in Red Flag was the Buccaneer, some of which were hastily applied with a coat of desert camouflage to suit the local terrain, and made them almost impossible to detect from above. *(Robbie Shaw)*

consistently well in all aspects of the competition, the features which had the most significant impact on the outcome were timing, which was plus/minus two seconds in a six and a half hour sortie; accuracy, which achieved errors of less than 30 feet during high speed, low level bombing runs; and effective jamming procedures.

Overseas deployments outside the European area by RAF first-line aircraft nowadays usually involve participation in Red Flag or Maple Flag exercises or competitions such as the one described above; routine deployments to bases in the Middle East and Far East ended in the early 1970s, when the UK Government abandoned its permanent military bases East of Suez. In fact, the last RAF fighters to operate in the Far East were the Lightnings of No. 74 Squadron, which was based in Singapore until 1972.

In August and September 1988, however, the RAF once again proved its ability to provide rapid reinforcement for Commonwealth allies in the Far East when four Tornado F.3s of No. 29 Squadron deployed to Australia via the Middle East and Malaysia. The Royal Air Force objective of this operation, named Exercise Golden Eagle, was to demonstrate the ability of the Tornado F.3 to deploy over very long distance and be able to fight on arrival (what the RAF calls tactical air power projection). Initially, the exercise was devised as a means of meeting Britain's air defence commitments within the five-nation defence agreement with Australia, New Zealand, Singapore and Malaysia; it was sixteen years since RAF fighters had participated in the five-nation Integrated Air Defence System (IADS).

On 21 August two Tornados left Coningsby and deployed to Seeb, in the Sultanate of Oman, being joined en route by two more aircraft which had already staged forward to Cyprus. After a night stop in Seeb all four aircraft proceeded to Butterworth, on the west coast of Malaysia, being tanked en route by TriStar K.1s of No. 216 Squadron. The Tornados participated in the IADS exercise until 12 September, operating alongside the F-18 Hornets of No. 77 Squadron RAAF. The four RAF fighters then deployed to Thailand, where they exercised with the F-5E Tiger IIs of the Royal Thai Air Force until 23 September, after which they transited to Singapore. Here the Tornados split into two pairs, one demonstrating at Halim, Indonesia, and the other visiting Subang Air Base near Kuala Lumpur, Malaysia.

On 6 October all four aircraft were together again for the flight from Singapore to Darwin, Australia. The aircraft were refuelled three times on the flight (4 hr 40 min), again by No. 216 Squadron's TriStars. On 7 October the aircraft left Darwin for Williamtown RAAF base, where they were a star attraction in the Australian Bicentennial Air Show. They stayed at Williamtown until 18 October, again exercising with the RAAF (this time No. 3 Squadron) before returning to the United Kingdom via Pago Pago (Samoa), Hickham Air Force Base in Hawaii, Travis AFB in California and Harrisburg AFB in Pennsylvania. They stayed at Harrisburg for four days, participating in the annual air show, and arrived back at RAF Coningsby on 20 October.

Exercise Golden Eagle was more than a further proof of the Tornado's effectiveness. It showed that, as a combat-ready force capable of operating anywhere in the world in support of Britain's allies, the RAF was back in business.

# CHAPTER ELEVEN
## Research and Development

**R**esearch and development is of fundamental importance to the efficiency of a high-technology fighting Service like the Royal Air Force. A high proportion of Government expenditure on R and D is concerned with military programmes, with the Ministry of Defence footing the bill. The most significant of the MoD's R and D establishments involved in aerospace are the Royal Aircraft Establishment, the Royal Signals and Radar Establishment, the Aeroplane and Armament Experimental Establishment, the Proof and Experimental Establishments, the Admiralty Surface Weapons Establishment and the Propellants, Explosives and Rocket Motor Establishment.

**The Royal Aircraft Establishment (RAE)** is the largest air systems research and development centre in Europe with responsibilities for the conduct and co-ordination of all military aerospace R and D with the exception of radar. RAE's expertise covers the whole range of disciplines fundamental to aerospace technology. Its work extends from conceptual through basic research to the evolution of operational techniques. It participates in development programmes of multi-national projects, is prominent in collaborative research and is frequently the technical agency for the exchange of information covered by government to government agreements. The RAE possesses a range of complex major facilities that today's aerospace technology demands for testing and calculations. In addition to Farnborough, these are sited at Bedford, Aberporth, Larkhill, West Freugh, Llanbedr and Pyestock. RAE Bedford has a large wind tunnel complex where advanced work is carried out on hypersonic flight and also on VSTOL aerodynamics; the airfield also houses the Blind Landing Experimental Unit (BLEU) and the flying wing of the Royal Signals and Radar Establishment.

Aberporth (Dyfed) is the site of the Rocket Research Establishment, the rocket range being at Llanbedr (Gwynedd). The RAE site at Larkhill in Wiltshire is involved in ballistics research, while RAE West Freugh's main function is weapons development trials with air-launched missiles. RAE Pyestock is the Government centre for R and D in gas turbines and related systems. It possesses in its altitude test cells the most comprehensive facilites in Europe for the full environmental testing of engines. Pyestock's broad objectives are to determine how engines can be made to consume less fuel, weigh less, be made more reliable, produce cleaner exhausts — a very important factor in military aircraft operation — and make less noise, which is equally as important in the environmental context.

**The Royal Signals and Radar Establishment (RSRE)** at Malvern is the MoD's main centre where research work is carried out on new electronic devices and their application, the aim being to bring about radical developments in electronic equipment for the Armed Services. The main systems activites in RSRE are airborne, battlefield and ground radar, opto-electronics, guided weapons, ground-based communications and air traffic control, the last of which is funded by the Civil Aviation Authority.

**The Directorate of Proof and Experimental Establishments (P and EE)** comprises a small London HQ and five establishments situated at Shoeburyness, Pendine, Eskmeals, Lavington and Inchterf. The Directorate has the responsibility for testing weapons for the Armed Services during both development and production. The large sea and land areas available to the Establishments, together with their associated airspace, enable projectiles and explosives and other potentially dangerous materials to be fired or tested safely. Results are fully recorded and analysed by the comprehensive equipment deployed. Shoeburyness is the largest of the P and EEs and conducts a wide variety of tests on missiles, missile motors, aircraft, aircraft components and aero-engines to assess their vulnerability to attack and to establish how effective various forms of attack are in damaging those items of equipment. Pendine features two high-speed rocket runways which are used to test aircraft components and warheads and the operation of guided and unguided weapons. Eskmeals has access to a vast sea area over which it is possible to fire projectiles at very long ranges; one of its major functions is the radar tracking of artillery projectiles to determine their range and accuracy data.

**The Propellants, Explosives and Rocket Motor Establishments (PERME)** is a major MoD R and D facility which undertakes research, exploratory development, project development and in some areas production, in the fields of rocket motors, rocket and gun propellants, gas generators, power cartridges and explosives for defence and civil purposes. PERME's work on rocket propulsion is supported mainly by BAJ Vickers Ltd, which undertakes research, development and production of rocket motor bodies, nozzles and other components, and by Royal Ordnance Factories (ROF) which carry out propellant manufacture and filling, igniter filling and the production of rocket motor hardware.

**The Aeroplane and Armament Experimental Establishment (A and AEE)** at Boscombe Down in Wiltshire is the MoD's centre for the acceptance testing of all military aircraft and associated equipment intended for use by Britain's Armed Services. It therefore forms a crucial link between those who build British military aircraft and those who fly them. Its task is to ensure that aircraft are safe and reliable, have the handling characteristics needed for their roles and that performance specifications are met. While the research and development associated with many of the items which go into modern military aircraft are undertaken by other establishments, it is at A and AEE that the complete aircraft weapons system is assessed against the requirements that have been laid down for it. Without the work of the A and AEE the RAF could not function as an effective fighting force, and its organisation and activities therefore merit examination in some detail.

The A and AEE has a unique combination of Service and civilian personnel which forms a closely knit team under the direction and leadership of the Commandant, who is an Air Commodore, and a civilian Chief Superintendent. It is composed of eight divisions, each headed by a Group Captain or civilian equivalent, supported by administrative services and a small RAF unit. The Empire Test Pilots' School (ETPS) is also integrated with A and AEE.

In its earlier days, the A and AEE only came into the picture after an aircraft had been produced in response to an Operational Requirement, when the Establishment carried out acceptance trials at the end of the development phase. Nowadays, the A and AEE staff liaise closely with industry, MoD and the Ministry of Technology from the earliest stages of any project and, at appropriate stages throughout the development, visit the manufacturer to make preview trials. This liaison extends internationally to such projects as Tornado and, most recently, the European Fighter Aircraft. Full co-operation and exchange of ideas is carried on with research establishments such as RAE Farnborough, the CSRE at Malvern, and with Service organisations such as the Central Servicing and Development Establishment at RAF Swanton Morley, the Central Reconnaissance Establishment at RAF Brampton and the Central Tactics and Trials Organisation. The latter, which forms part of Strike Command HQ at High Wycombe, is responsible for the conduct of trials and the development of tactics for all RAF operational aircraft.

The primary function of the A and AEE is to test and assess. Its responsibilities are to maintain the highest standards of assessment and to make recommendations as to the suitability or otherwise of the test subject. It has no executive authority; it is the testing agency of the Ministry of Technology, which in turn is the procuring agent for the Ministry of Defence, and the Establishment can only recommend to Mintech that the product is acceptable or otherwise and that in its opinion certain modifications or limitations are acceptable or desirable. Many factors can, and do, outweight A and AEE's recommendations and consequently the product as issued is not always what it might have been were, for example, time and cost considerations less stringent.

Of the A and AEE's various divisions, the Trials Management Division is responsible for the planning, control and co-ordination of the Establishment's effort on the advanced projects with which it is involved from the early design stages. Currently, these include projects such as the EFA and the EH.101 helicopter, and also updates of existing in-service types like the Harrier and Tornado.

The Performance Division is responsible for the conduct of the aerodynamic and thermo-dynamic assessment of the complete aircraft to provide recommendations on operating limitations and operating data. It becomes involved in the early stages of an aircraft's flight development to assess progress and to advise both the manufacturer and Mintech on areas where improvement may be required. Its assessment of an aircraft's flying qualities ultimately covers the full flight envelope of height, speed, Mach number, centre of gravity, weight and normal acceleration and includes tests appropriate to the category of aircraft — for example, spinning and aerobatics on trainers and transient effects during supply dropping.

An example of the Performance Division's work involved the Sepecat Jaguar; when this aircraft was being assessed by the A and AEE pilots prior to its entry into RAF service, they recommended that it should not be cleared for diving at the ground, which was a somewhat severe restriction to impose upon a ground attack/strike aircraft, even though it was designed with a flat first-run attack in mind. The A and AEE found that as g was applied, the aircraft rolled. The rate of roll was just acceptable on a clean aircraft, but with weapons on the flick could be as much as 180 degrees, and under certain circumstances 360 degrees. It was discovered that the problem was caused by the fuselage flexing under g, causing the rudder to move and bring on yaw-roll coupling. With weapons on, the roll rate increased to an extent that normal anti-roll control application could not cope. The problem was remedied in three stages: spine-bending compensation, coupling the rudder with the roll control and making the control column longer.

The Royal Aerospace Establishment (RAE) operates an interesting and diverse fleet of aircraft, including a Dakota. *(Robbie Shaw)*

A more recent example involved trying to find ways of increasing the Nimrod MR.2's crosswind landing limits, particularly on short runways. Both British Aerospace and the A and AEE worked on this problem, with classified results.

The Engineering Division is responsible for the safety, efficiency and reliability of all systems in an aircraft apart from those related to armament, navaids, radio and photographic equipment. The Division's test equipment includes a large open jet wind tunnel for tests on the ground at speeds of up to 350 knots to assess canopy release, ejections through the canopy, sequenced ejection and manual bale-out; a specially modified Canberra from which both gun and rocket ejection seats can be fired at speeds of up to 450 knots; and an environmental test hangar which is capable of simulating full tropical climatic conditions. The Division is also responsible for the final development and clearance of paratrooping and supply-dropping techniques and equipments. For example, the Division put in a considerable amount of work in clearing the 'stretched' Hercules C.3 for supply dropping; it was found that when dropping a stream of one-ton containers, the fifteen-foot-longer load-travel momentarily placed the C of G a long way outside its limits, and so a new handling technique had to be devised to compenste for this.

The Armament Division is responsible for the safe and reliable carriage and release of weapons from aircraft, throughout the required flight envelopes. This work involves the assessment of the electrical and mechanical engineering of the armament installation (bombs, guns, rockets, guided weaponry), integrity of carriage in flight, safe and clean separation and, as appropriate, the feeding of the necessary fusing functions into the weapons. The Division is also responsible for the assessment of the electro-magnetic compatibility of weapons and aircraft, since instances have occurred where a radar or radio transmission has caused electrically initiated explosive devices to fire.

Also located at Boscombe is the Empire Test Pilots' School which trains test pilots not only for the British Forces, but for a number of other friendly countries. One of the types used is the Hawk T1, painted in the attractive 'raspberry ripple' scheme. *(Robbie Shaw)*

The A and AEE's weapons release trials have produced some interesting problems over the years. Apart from problems with the boundary layer and localised flow, other factors can also affect release. The weaponry carried by the Tornado, for example, tends to pitch up sharply on separation. Going back a good many more years, the release of conventional bombs from the Vickers Valiant produced a classic example of the unforeseen problems that can occur. The Valiant's bomb bay was designed to carry the 10,000 lb MC.Mk 1 nuclear store (Blue Danube), but when 1,000 lb iron bombs were released they were suspended for several seconds in the airflow, which did nothing for bombing accuracy. The problem was solved by fitting a baffle forward of the bomb bay, which extended when the bomb doors were opened.

Armament trials begin on the ground, with the weapons being mated to the aircraft for the first time. Once the weapons fit is shown to be compatible with the aircraft, which is not always the case, the aircraft is towed over to a special pit and the weapons are filmed with a high-speed cine camera as they release. This drop provides valuable data, under still-air conditions, on the natural pitch, roll and yaw of the weapon and the arming wire's angle of pull-off. Some trials have shown that the arming wires flail, or the electrical impulse which arms the weapon arrives just after the wire has parted. These snags can be rectified before the airborne trials phase begins, the angle of pull-off being set up and the ejector rams set up to counteract still-air pitch. After this has been achieved satisfactorily, the weapon is fitted with pressure and vibration transducers and flown.

At the RAE Bedford radar research is carried out, mostly using some interesting Canberras, such as this B6 MOD. *(Robbie Shaw)*

The next phase is to investigate the aircraft's handling with symmetric and asymmetric loads, then the programme moves on to release trials in which the weapons are released singly or in sequence. This is followed by jettison trials, when the weapons can be dropped sequentially or released almost simultaneously. Bombs and missiles pose few problems on jettison because their weight remains constant, but items such as rocket pods and fuel tanks can have greatly differing weight values depending on their expenditure and as a result their jettison characteristics can be unpredictable. Trials with the SNEB rocket pod for the Harrier showed an alarming tendency for a partially full pod to pitch up sharply and roll along the wing. (The SNEB rocket pod is no longer used by the Harrier Force assigned to NATO, but is retained by the Belize detachment.)

Tactical nuclear weapons — or more correctly in this context bomb 'shapes' with dummy warheads to the exact weight of the real thing — are subjected to similar but more stringent trials, with all systems required to be proved three times and subject to an independent check by the Ordnance Board. Release speeds associated with nuclear weapons are generally higher, so that the aircraft can get clear before detonation.

The three months of the Falklands War, including the preparatory period, in 1982 saw Boscombe Down involved in frenetic activity, carrying out essential work on clearing modifications to in-service aircraft. These mainly involved the proving of ECM, flight refuelling and missile systems for carriage by aircraft such as the Nimrod and Vulcan but many other associated items had to be dealt with. Some of the concepts that originated in the Falklands War are still being proved today.

One of the Armament Division's biggest on-going programmes has been concerned with the Nimrod MR.2, whose systems are so complex that clearance work on necessary modifications to them, in order to keep abreast of current threats, will continue throughout the aircraft's in-service life. Nimrod MR.2 Weapon System Performance Trials were (and still are, as new weapons are cleared for use by the aircraft) carried out at a fully instrumented test range just

At Boscombe Down the Aeroplane and Armament Experimental Establishment (A&AEE) carries out research flying on aircraft, weapons and aircraft systems prior to entry to RAF service. A varied fleet of aircraft is used, such as this Hunter FGA9. *(Robbie Shaw)*

east of Andros Island in the Bahamas, owned by the US Navy Underwater Systems Center. Nimrods deployed there are based at Homestead AFB, south of Miami. The facility is excellent for this type of work; the depth of water averages 4,800 feet, and surrounding island chains tend to keep shipping away, so that the water is quiet for sonar trials.

An area of sea bed 35 nm long and 5 nm wide is sown with sonar sensors, which can track a submarine or torpedo to within fifteen to twenty feet. At the same time, transponder-equipped aircraft can be tracked to within 100 feet, up to 70,000 feet altitude, so that the test data can be compiled into a very accurate plot showing the relative positions of aircraft, submarines, sonobuoys and torpedoes. The main aim of the weapons trials in the mid-1980s was to assess the Stingray lightweight torpedo in the air-dropped role, and also to prove the Nimrod's compatibility with various air-launched missiles including the Harpoon anti-ship missile and the Sidewinder AAM, the latter having been fitted as an emergency self-defence measure during the Falklands campaign.

The A and AEE's Navigation and Radio Division is responsible for the acceptance trials of Navigation/Attack and Radio/Radar installations in new military aircraft and equipments introduced by retrofit action into existing military aircraft. It is also concerned with the evaluation of new equipments and systems being considered for possible installation in future military aircraft and with the evaluation of selected civil navigation systems. The Division has undertaken much work in finding an effective means of shielding an aircraft from the electro-magnetic pulse (EMP), which is generated by the explosion of a nuclear weapon and which can play havoc with modern avionics, and against spurious radio-frequency transmissions which are generated inside the aircraft itself and which can cause all manner of problems, including the accidental release or firing of weapons. This work is carried out in close conjunction with the Armament Division.

The Photographic Trials and Facilities Division is responsible for the testing of new photographic equipment and photographic reconnaissance installations, while the task of the Technical Services Division is to keep the A and AEE's large, varied and constantly changing aircraft fleet serviceable.

All flying for the trials divisions of the A and AEE is carried out by the Flying Division, which is divided into squadrons according to function and role. The constitution of the squadrons is adjusted from time to time to ensure that the span of control is effective for the current work load. 'A' Squadron is responsible for fighter/strike and training aircraft; 'B' Squadron for maritime aircraft; 'C' Squadron for naval fixed wing aircraft; 'D' Squadron for helicopters, and 'E' Squadron for transport aircraft. There is also a Transport Flight which operates in support of overseas trials. Together, the Squadrons operate every aircraft on the RAF's inventory, with the exception of some of the older helicopters, trainers and communications types.

# CHAPTER TWELVE
## The Royal Air Force in Space

United Kingdom involvement with military satellite communications started in the 1960s with participation in the United States Initial Defence Satellite Communications Program (IDSCP). Work in this multiple orbiting satellite-based system led to the UK pioneering the use of a geostationary satellite to support defence communications, Skynet 1. This was followed in 1974 by the more capable Skynet 2B, which still has an operating payload. A change in government policy removed the requirement for communications to permanent garrison areas east of Suez, which then formed a large part of the Skynet role. The Skynet 3 programme was cancelled and the reduced space segment requirements, with the emphasis on NATO areas, were satisfied by arrangements within the Alliance. The advance of technology soon permitted the development of a range of tactical terminals whose deployment would be constrained by the limited space segment available.

In 1981 the British Ministry of Defence decided to proceed with a new generation of spacecraft, Skynet 4. British Aerospace was selected to be prime contractor and Marconi Space Systems tasked with providing the specialised communications equipment. Three Skynet 4 spacecraft have been built, all scheduled to be operational with the British Services by the end of 1990; the first was launched from Kourou, French Guiana, on 9 December 1988 using an Ariane 4 rocket (Flight V27).

On station at one degree West, the spacecraft provided the UK's armed forces with a radio relay in space, with greatly increased strategic and tactical communications capacity and improved anti-jamming capability. Operating in SHF and UHF frequency bands, Skynet's antennae provide a variety of footprints ranging from spot to global coverage. This variety of spot and global beams enables Skynet 4 satellites to serve an extensive inventory of earth stations ranging from small manpack sets to aircraft terminals, widely dispersed naval vessels and large anchor stations.

The principal anchor station is at RAF Oakhanger, in Hampshire, which is under the control of Support Command's No. 90 (Signals) Group. As prime contractor for the Skynet 2 satellite, Marconi Space Systems was responsible for the ground control facilities for that series of satellites, and the company's contribution to the ground control of Skynet 4 includes the supply of a new dual Satellite Operating Facility at Oakhanger. This Satellite Operating Facility provides a number of vital functions, including continuous monitoring of spacecraft telemetry and the secure command and control of all of the Satellite's sub-systems and station keeping. Marconi also provides Range Measurement Units which are employed to maintain accurate spacecraft station keeping in orbit, plus a comprehensive satellite payload simulator, an essential feature in the calibration of ground control facilities.

In September 1988, British Aerospace announced the award of a contract to design and build a satellite ground control centre for the MoD ar RAF Oakhanger; the centre will have multi-satellite control capability to be used with the three Skynet 4 satellites.

Complementing the development of the Skynet spacecraft itself, the past twenty years have seen the United Kingdom's armed forces progressively equipped with a comprehensive inventory of fixed and mobile Earth stations. The only truly fixed station is the Type 1 at Oakhanger itself. The Type 2 station, which has a forty-foot dish, can be recovered and redeployed to prepared sites; the Type 3 station has a twenty-foot dish and is air-portable to prepared sites in Hercules aircraft. In order to match the receiver performance of the bigger stations, it uses liquid nitrogen-cooled parametric amplifiers to reduce the system noise. The Type 4 station, which is operated by the Army, is truly air-portable; one station can be uplifted in a single Hercules and a link can be set up within a few hours of arriving on site. The station can also be broken down into sections to be carried by helicopters. The Type 5 station, which has a smaller communications capacity, is operated by the Royal Navy.

The responsibilities of the Royal Air Force in connection with the Skynet system include installation design, overall engineering management of the system, management and control of the spacecraft, and operation of the UK terminal at RAF Oakhanger, which is designated as a Telemetry and Command Station.

The Skynet 4 spacecraft is based on the highly successful three-axis stabilised platform developed by British Aerospace for the OTS/ECS and MARECS programmes. The same platform was used by the French PTT for its first generation of Telecom satellites. Skynet is of modular construction, comprising a service module which provides the satellite with housekeeping and orbital control functions. Connected to the service module are two solar arrays which rotate about their axis to follow the Sun and provide electrical power for the operation of the satellite and its payload. Mounted on top of the service module is the communications module, carrying the communications payload housing the transponders and antennae which permanently point towards Earth. This equipment includes an SHF package of three transponders, each of forty watts power providing four channels at bandwidths from 60 to 135 mHz; a UHF package of two transponders of forty watts, each serving one channel of 25 kHz bandwidth; and an EHF uplink channel for propagation experiments for future EHF systems.

The Skynet 4 spacecraft series was originally scheduled and designed for launch aboard the US Space Shuttle, which would also have carried a British payload specialist as part of its crew. A team of four specialists was selected, including Squadron Leader Nigel Wood, RAF. Despite the revival of the Space Shuttle programme, none of the Skynets will be launched by this method; the second was launched by Titan 3 in December 1989 and the third is due to be launched by Ariane 4 in June 1990. The disruption caused to the launch schedule by the destruction of the Challenger Orbiter in January 1986 necessitated modification of the Skynet spacecraft, mainly relating to solar panel procedures and deployment techniques.

It appears, at the time of writing, that the RAF's commitment in space is destined to remain solely in the field of satellite communications, unless at some future date RAF astronauts are selected to fly alongside their US counterparts on military missions in Shuttle-type spacecraft.

In a different sense, another RAF ground-based establishment performs a key role in space. This is the UK component of the Ballistic Missile Early Warning System at RAF Fylingdales, in North Yorkshire. In addition to its primary role, which is to give advance warning of IRBMs launched against the UK and Western Europe and of ICBMs launched against the North American continent, Fylingdales also tracks satellites and space debris. The latter is an increasingly important function, because in the latter part of 1988 there were some 5,400 pieces of trackable space debris in Earth orbit, together with 1,762 spacecraft, many of which were not operational — not to mention about 30,000 untrackable fragments of debris, Fylingdales' radar system is capable of detecting objects down to ten centimetres in diameter.

# CHAPTER THIRTEEN
## Looking to the Future

T he Royal Air Force was the first armed service in the world to apply scientific method in a systematic and organised way to the study of the art of warfare, and maintains this lead today.

In the Air Force Department of the Ministry of Defence there are two major cells, under the overall professional directorship of the Chief Scientist (RAF), one to deal with operational research into future operations, policy, equipment and logistics, and another which concerns itself with personnel recruitment, selection and training. The latter branch, consisting of a team of psychologists and supporting Service and civilian staff, advises on such matters as pre-selection pilot aptitude tests, as well as ground trade aptitude and social psychology, and evaluates the effectiveness of current training to the extent of recommending new training methods where these prove to be necessary.

At Command level, the operational research teams perform a vital task in collecting practical data on aircraft and personnel under conditions as near to wartime as it is possible to create in peace. In this field, the RAF is ahead of other countries. Operational Capability Trials are carried out on aircraft as an entity, as distinct from trials to prove the components of the aircraft, and as they result in a real assessment of how the aircraft would perform in time of war, they are of immense value in studying future projects. Tactical Evaluation Trials are also carried out, which study the performance of the whole aircraft in its operational environment, and result in quantifiable analysis of how, for example, an aircraft such as the Hawk would integrate into the total air defence environment. Finally, major defence exercises are carried out which simulate different aspects of possible wars.

The concepts of future RAF operations and of future aircraft requirements arise from a dialogue between the Service and the team of scientists which specialises in the future role of air power. Extensive use is made of computer simulations of future war situations, and these studies examine the validity of different concepts of operations and show the sort of requirements which a new aircraft should be designed to meet. This enables the Air Staff to formulate a provisional operational requirement, or Air Staff Target.

The choice of the Harrier and Tornado, both of which feature prominently in the RAF's front line and will continue to do so for many more years, provides an interesting example of the process leading up to an Air Staff Target. In the case of the Harrier, the aircraft was already being developed when operational research started in 1963. The question then was whether or not V/STOL aircraft would prove a cost-effective method of carrying out close air support operations. A mathematical model of the environment in which such an aircraft would operate was produced, based on the threat of a limited war east of Suez. The model took account of such things as the size of the threat, the performance of enemy aircraft and the cabability of our air defences, all in widely different geographic situations.

An important parameter in the research was the survivability of the close air support force to pre-emptive enemy attack, and a vital input in this respect came from practical flying trials which were carried out in the Middle East to assess the probability of the enemy detecting randomly dispersed V/STOL aircraft. The trials provided data on the probability of detection at different ranges from the searching aircraft, and showed that it would be very difficult for an enemy to detect the Harrier, compared with short or conventional take-off aircraft which did not lend themselves to such a high degree of dispersal.

Cost-effective comparisons were then made between VTOL, STOL and conventional take-off aircraft of similar performance in terms of the ability to deliver the required weapon load to the target. The results showed that an aircraft with VTOL capability was the cheapest way of delivering a given weight of weapons to a target for all sizes of enemy threat and of our air defence deployment. They also showed, however, that a point could be reached with a very large threat or air defence deployment, where the Harrier would not be the best choice. Therefore, when the emphasis of Britain's defence switched from East of Suez to Europe, the project was reassessed in view of the increased size of the enemy threat in that theatre and the improved defence system available to the West. This reassessment indicated that, within the Harrier's lifetime at least, VTOL would still prove the best choice, but not by such a large margin.

In the 1970s, with major improvements taking place in the Warsaw Pact countries' offensive systems, the question of VTOL as a future requirement in the close support role was re-examined.

Below: On the airshow scene probably the two most popular items are the Red Arrows and the Battle of Britain Memorial Flight. *(Robbie Shaw)*

Overleaf: A Spitfire escorts the Lancaster during an airshow flypast. *(Robbie Shaw)*

The result of the reappraisal was favourable, and led to the decision to develop the Harrier GR.5 for the RAF.

The operational research which eventually led to the requirement for the Tornado started in 1967/68, when the RAF carried out investigations into the feasibility of counter-air operations (attacking enemy airfields) and interdiction operations through the 1980s. A comprehensive computer simulation was constructed to represent a series of realistic attacks on certain airfields and interdiction targets. Factors taken into account in programming the computer included the air defence threat from anti-aircraft guns, surface to air missiles, and fighter aircraft, giving credit for the most technologically advanced systems which could be possible within the timescale, but which, in fact, might not necessarily be met.

Having programmed the worst possible conditions for aircraft attacks, these were then staged against various targets, including dispersed aircraft, aircraft in revetments and in shelters, and the take-off and landing areas; interdiction targets such as bridges were also considered. A range of attack aircraft were studied, some of which were assumed to be developments of exisiting types, such as the Buccaneer, Phantom and Jaguar. Based on the extensive studies which had already been carried out into the Anglo-French Variable Geometry Aircraft, other types of attack aircraft were assumed to have a similar configuration. A variety of avionic and ECM equipments were considered, from those with current capabilities to those likely to be available within the current timescale.

The computer programme included numerous tactical options, such as defence saturation, penetration altitudes from very high to very low, a wide range of routeings around defences, cities, airfields and so on. Also considered were the effects of fighter sweeps before the raids, fighter cover with the attacking aircraft, spoof raids before the attack and dilution of the attacking force by including cheap aircraft to increase defence saturation and to spread the losses, thereby possibly increasing the chances of a higher proportion of the attacking aircraft reaching the target. It was assumed that in the attack, ECM would be used to jam ground and airborne radars, and to decoy missiles, and different penetration speeds were used at different heights below 500 feet, using terrain-following radar to provide a night and all-weather capability.

Enemy defensive tactics were also taken into account during these studies, and in all cases the potential enemy was given the most effective tactics and defences that could be devised.

Step by step, the computer simulation traced the path of the aircraft from take-off, through the phase of the flight cruise to the enemy border, the high-speed dash to the target, and eventual return and recovery to base. The chances of success were evaluated within a vast number of permutations of the different parameters involved. The results showed, under various conditions, the number of aircraft which started out, those which were likely to reach the target, and the number which were likely to return to base.

Estimates of the effectiveness of those aircraft which reached the target were, if anything, conservative in their assumptions regarding future weapons available to the force. Knowing how many weapons would be needed to inflict the required damage on the target, and therefore how many aircraft would be required to reach the target, it was possible to calculate how many aircraft of a given type must be launched at the start of the attack. The results showed that the losses and force requirements were such that counter air and interdiction operations remained a feasible proposition into the 1990s.

The requirements for a new generation aircraft for this role, to minimise the force losses and therefore the total force requirement, were shown to point the need for either a new Buccaneer, or for the Multi-Role Combat Aircraft (MRCA), as the Tornado was then known. However, when similar computer studies were carried out for reconnaissance operations, it became clear that only the MRCA could meet all the requirements. Previous studies had also indicated that fighter aircraft with supersonic performance were essential, and again the MRCA specification called for this ability; this was the origin of the Tornado ADV, which today is No. 11 Group's first line of defence.

Hurricane and Lancaster of the Battle of Britain Memorial Flight based at Coningsby.
*(Robbie Shaw)*

Subsequent operational research has pointed out firm requirements for sophisticated fighter aircraft, crystallized in the EFA, for counter-air and interdiction aircraft beyond Tornado in the twenty-first century, and for long-range maritime patrol aircraft — possibly a variant of the FIMA advanced transport aircraft project. But what about other roles for air power?

Studies are now being undertaken to assess the levels of sophistication required for future aircraft in the Army close support role, with particular reference to the future need for a vertical take-off capability in relation to cost. Other lines of research are investigating whether aircraft speed is as critical in close support aircraft as it is in those making deeper penetrations into enemy territory, whether a sophisticated nav/attack system is essential in an aircraft which has to search for its target visually, and whether range/payload requirements can be reduced, bearing in mind that many Army targets are likely to be close to the forward edge of the battle area. This facet of research is particularly important, since the increasing tendency to sophistication in military aircraft has resulted in smaller and smaller front line strengths. It is therefore vital to carry out a fundamental reappraisal of the real need for different levels of sophistication, as any reduction in sophistication will result in cheaper aircraft and consequently greater front-line strengths. In the final analysis, the choice comes down to advanced, supersonic STOVL, or to the small agile battlefield aircraft (the SABA, described earlier in this book) or an appropriate mix of both.

Corporal Steve Wood with the Parade Bass Drum of the RAF's Central Band based at Uxbridge. *(Robbie Shaw)*

The Department of the Chief Scientist (RAF) and the Operational Requirements Branch of MoD (Air) are also extending these lines of research to other, future combat aircraft which will form the backbone of the Royal Air Force in the next century. The details of this research must remain secret; but what is happening behind the scenes today will ensure that the Royal Air Force will have the best equipment, and that it will be able to use it in the most effective manner to counter any threat to our national security that may arise in years to come.

# INDEX